Salt

C000103148

Silk

by

D Meredith McFadden

With special acknowledgement to
Researcher & Genealogist Pam Buttrey

© D Meredith McFadden 2005
Salt & Silk
ISBN 0-9549582-0-9

Published by:
Aubrey Warsash Publications
PO Box 3186
South Croydon
Surrey
CR2 6UW
United Kingdom

Design & production co-ordinated by:
The *Better Book* Company Ltd
Havant
Hampshire
PO9 2XH

Printed in England

Contents

Foreword

I have eaten your bread and salt.
I have drunk your water and wine.
The deaths ye died I have watched beside
And the lives ye led were mine.

Rudyard Kipling, 1886

The sources of the principal facts concerning the lives of the Salter and the Royalist M.P. are listed at the end of the book, for these two men, one a great-grandson of the other, actually existed.

As well, over twelve generations of the Salter's descendants have been traced and documented down to the present day.

Much we know for certain.

However, there are inevitable gaps in the surviving records relating to the lives of Morgan Aubrey the Salter and Herbert Aubrey the Royalist and these have been filled with fictionalised episodes, scenes and conversations.

For example, Clehonger Manor was in fact a Royalist garrison during the English Civil War, but there is no record of the Scots army, which besieged Hereford for six weeks, ever occupying the house.

Nor can we find evidence of Thomas, the Royalist's brother, being given a position as a scribe with the influential Sir Robert Clayton, one of the wealthiest men in England at the time.

We do know for sure though, that Herbert wrote that letter of sympathy to Lord Danby when he was incarcerated in the Tower, but whether the promised 'small collar of brawn' and the 'cyder' ever found its way to the prisoner, we can only assume and hope that the answer was in fact, 'Yes, it did'.

As a nineteenth-century historian once remarked, 'Faithfulness to the truth of history involves far more than research, however scrupulous... the narrator must seek to imbue himself with the life and spirit of the time.'

This is what I have sought to do. D Meredith McFadden

HEREFORDSHIRE

The Aubreys of Clehonger

MORGAN AUBREY (c1527-1608) Salter and Citizen of London. Married JOAN VAUX (d.1614) daughter of Robert Vaux of Cumberland. Bought Clehonger estate in 1594. Had a daughter KATHERINE and a son,

Sir SAMUEL AUBREY (1580-1645) of Clehonger. Married JOYCE RUDHALL (c1585-1638) daughter of William Rudhall of Rudhall. Had two sons, MORGAN and ANTHONY and a daughter JOANE who married Thomas Emley of Helmdon, Northamptonshire. His heir,

HERBERT AUBREY I (1603-1671) of Clehonger, married ELIZABETH BEDELL (1609-1675) daughter of Mathew Bedell of London. Of their daughters, ANNE married William Boothby and ELIZABETH died unmarried. Of their sons, GODWIN married Joan Clark, and THOMAS died unmarried. His heir,

HERBERT AUBREY II (1631-1691) M.P., of Clehonger, married JOYCE BRYDGES (1638-1712) daughter of John Brydges of Priors Court. Their sons were BYRDGES and REGINALD. The latter married Elizabeth Bubb. Of their two daughters, ELIZABETH died unmarried and the other, JOYCE, married Gilbert Hearne of Hereford.

HERBERT AUBREY III (1664-1744) of Clehonger. Married three times: firstly to JUDITH COLE (1666-1706) daughter of Thomas Cole of Liss in Hampshire; secondly to Rebecca Gwillym widow of John Evans; thirdly to Debora Hopton widow of William Delahay. His only child was by his first wife,

HERBERT AUBREY IV (1693-1758) of Clehonger. Married firstly ARABELLA HARCOURT (1685-1749) daughter of Simon Viscount Harcourt; secondly Ann Jones, widow of Richard Fleming by whom he had no children. Arabella produced five daughters: JUDITH and ARABELLA who died unmarried; ELIZABETH who married her cousin Gilbert Hearne; DOROTHEA who married Moore Green of Cagebrook, and ANNE who married Percival Lloyd of Ingeston. Herbert's only son was:

HARCOURT AUBREY (1725-1779) of Clehonger. Married ELIZABETH MORSE (1735-1780), daughter of Richard Morse of Hereford. They had two daughters,

ELIZABETH who married GABRIEL WYNNE (d.1814), and MARTHA who married JOHN WYNNE, probably brothers. Both men changed their names to Aubrey and most subsequent generations were known as Wynne Aubrey. Harcourt's son and heir was,

RICHARD AUBREY (1757-1803) of Liss Place and Clehonger. He died unmarried, his sisters Elizabeth and Martha becoming his heirs.

ELIZABETH WYNNE (1758-1831) produced four daughters: CAROLINE ELIZA who married Frederick William Lawday; LOUISA who died unmarried; EMILY who married William Dampier; and ANNA MARIA who married Lt.Timothy Macnamara, R.N. Of her sons, the eldest RICHARD died aged 19. Her other sons were FREDERICK WYNNE AUBREY and his older brother HENRY HARCOURT WYNNE AUBREY, who became Elizabeth's nominal heir.

MARTHA WYNNE (1763-1827) married three times. By her first husband she had a daughter CHARLOTTE who married firstly Jonathon Elford and then Giovanni Bezzi. There were no children from Martha's marriages to Rev. Daniel Griffiths of Broom Hall, and Henry Pinson Tozer. Both Bezzi and Tozer added Aubrey to their names.

HENRY HARCOURT WYNNE AUBREY (1788-1860) Soldier and adventurer who led a flamboyant and sometimes dangerous existence. Eloped with heiress BARBARA BROWN (1798-1882) daughter of Patrick Brown of Edinburgh. She bore sixteen children before divorcing him. Henry's younger brother was,

FREDERICK WYNNE AUBREY (1793-1852) 'of Clehonger', soldier and lawyer. Married LOUISA MOORE (1806-1848) daughter of Capt. John Moore, 3rd Regt. Dragoon Guards. She bore six children. Frederick involved himself in litigation over the Aubrey properties for more than twenty years. One of his daughters,

ELIZABETH ANNE AMELIA AUBREY (1827-1888) went to India where she married LACHLAN MACLEAN (1827-1884), General Assistant Surgeon, Bengal Medical Services, East India Co. Armies. She bore the first of her five children at the height of the Indian Mutiny. Later, the family lived in France, the Channel Islands, New Zealand and Australia. At her death, Elizabeth left a small fortune to her offspring - but only to those whom she considered worthy enough to inherit her money.

Acknowledgements

A great many people, most of them unknown to us, have helped over the years with information relating to the Aubreys of Clehonger. They include the staff of the British Library, National Archives, Guildhall Library, Family Record Centre, Northamptonshire Record Office, Herefordshire Record Office, Croydon Local Studies Library, Society of Genealogists, and the Herefordshire Family History Society, for which we have been most grateful.

On a personal note, I should like to express my thanks for the assistance given by Colonel Michael Barneby, Clerk to the Salters' Company, Sian Mogridge of the Corporation of London Records Office, Alex Buchanan, Archivist of the Clothworker's Company, Brian Prosser, Marsha Barnsley and Frances Stroud of Clehonger, and Dr Peter Russell also of Clehonger.

Historian Roland Thorne, and niece Dairneen (aka Neen) and John Roberts have always given support and encouragement, and this has been much appreciated.

I am especially indebted to Bill McFadden, for without him, none of this would have been possible.

Lastly, my grateful thanks go to Researcher and Genealogist Pam Buttrey, a friend of many years' standing. She has been involved with this book from its inception and has tracked down nearly all the records relating to the Aubreys of Clehonger and beyond.

Picture and other acknowledgements:

Rudyard Kipling's lines from his Prelude to Departmental Ditties and other Verses, courtesy of A P Watt Ltd on behalf of The National Trust for Places of Historic Interest or Natural Beauty;

Wenceslaus Hollar's Execution of Thomas Earle of Strafford, courtesy of the Guildhall Library, Corporation of London;

St Mary Abchurch Burial Register of 1565, courtesy of the Guildhall Library, Corporation of London;

Salters' Crest, courtesy of Colonel Michael Barneby, Clerk to the Salters' Company;

Map of Herefordshire, courtesy of Byron Theodore of Port Macquarie, N.S.W.

Salt & Silk

Morgan Aubrey

Salter & Citizen of London

Morgan Aubrey (c1527-1608) = Joan Holman née Vaux (d.1614)

(Sir) Samuel Aubrey (1580-1645)   Katherine (Kate) (1572-1617)
= Joyce Rudhall (c1585-1638)   =1) Dr Francis Bevans (d.1602)
                                   =2) Sir William Herbert
                                          (c1539-1609)
                                  =3) Sir Anthony St John
                                          (d.1638)

1. Herbert Aubrey (1603-1671)
= Elizabeth Bedell (1609-1676)

2. Morgan (1607-1641) Slain in Ireland

3. Anthony (d.1679)

4. Joane (b.c1606) = Thomas Emley of Helmdeon, Northants

Anno Domini 1565

The last two lines read: 'Joan Sheffell servant with Morgan Awberry buried ye 21st May'; 'Margerie the daughter of Morgan Awbery buried ye 15th June'. (Guildhall Library Ms 7666)

1. London Beckons

My name is Morgan Aubrey and this chronicle is at once mine, and that of the children of my children. In the bloom of youth and in my dreams of the future, I their progenitor, saw these little ones, soon now to live again, as nine stars each further away in the heavens from the last, but all linked by a line of blood, mine.

There on earth, out of the boundary of space or time, when the past has mocked us all, we have been given again the breath of life. Each one played his role in the world, living out his allotted span, blessed or cursed as God ordained – and with a tale to tell.

My own second coming on these pages, pales in comparison with my first, when I left my mother's womb as the son of William Aubrey of Abercynrig and Maud, the daughter of Philip of Glyntarrel. There, in that little Welsh village of small cottages with ageing thatch, dominated by the parish church overlooking the green, dedicated to the Celtic Saint Brynach, I once walked and rode, laughed and cried; I lived and breathed and had my being in the flesh. We know who we are, but know not who we may be. Apt words in this case, from the mouth of the young man playing the part of Ophelia.

I remember Joan insisting we see William Shakespeare's play at the Globe Theatre, even though it meant us leaving Candlewick Street in good time and making our way to the other side of the Thames. The story of a prince of Denmark held little interest for me, but I had early learnt that objections to my dear wife's wishes always came at a price, so off we set.

At that time I walked with the aid of a stick, which slowed my gait somewhat. I told Joan I carried it just to ward off any cutpurses who barred my path, but she jokingly called it 'my third leg'. She paid the waterman well – first checking his licence - to see us safely across the Thames to Bankside and back and so for some hours, in that little wooden "O", we were transported in our thoughts to Elsinore Castle. But I digress, memories playing strange games with a life, now twice lived.

God gave me a quick mind, and a ready disposition and although my bones have long since been pounded into the London dust when the burial grounds of St Mary Abchurch fell victim to encroaching buildings and roads, they were once of a man somewhat short in stature. I never forgot my Welsh tongue, which forced me to speak English in a way that those I would meet on my travels, would identify me as a Welshman. Not that I was ever ashamed of being one, especially since Henry Tudor triumphed over King Richard III at Bosworth. A divine victory for the race that can trace its origins back to Simon of Troy, or in our family's case, the Counts of Boulogne and Danmartin when we were known before the Conquest by the Norman name de Alberico.

I grew up at Abercynrig in the parish of Llanfrynach that still nestles comfortably beside the River Usk in the shadow of the Brecon Beacons. In my mind's eye, as I remember the prince's friend saying of the ghost, I can still see the green fields rolling towards the watchful, purple hills, stark against the sky. On a clear day from a high window of our house, I could watch the Cynrig across the meadows, rising below Pen y Fân and rushing down to join the River Usk, as if in a hurry to leave those Welsh hills behind and surge into bigger waters. Water flowed aplenty near the house too: a pond and three springs gave life to the orchards and the flowers growing in abundance in the nearby fields.

Lush and green as they were, I early on had set my sights on London. My brother Hopkin and his farm, locked into the vagaries of the seasons in that Welsh valley, held no interest for me, and thoughts of my father – well, they set my blood racing for many a year after I left the land of my birth.

I went to the English capital, as every young person does, who wants to grasp hold of life and make something of himself. I vowed to make money there, marry, purchase land near the Welsh border and prosper for my children, should God so bless me. In truth though, London provided a simple excuse for leaving a hated father and a maligned mother.

No man whose father has wronged him can ever see the world through confident eyes. One is suckled by one's mother or wet nurse, but in the power behind the love behind the nipple, looms one's father. You take his name, and if the stars are in the right place at your birth, you eventually inherit his land.

Mine were not, and I even felt a curse had been put upon me. My father, ever a jealous man, had renounced my mother on a trumped up charge of infidelity, on the strength of which, had angrily disinherited us. His new wife Jane, the woman who so easily had usurped our mother's place, enjoyed her position as the daughter of Sir Richard Herbert of Cwmystwith, a proud and wealthy man.

It seemed no time at all before she gave my father a son. They called him Richard and to my secret disappointment, he thrived. Then came a daughter named Janet. Richard would now inherit Abercynrig, the place that had been in our family for generations and for this I hated him.

When I allowed my father's betrayal to overwhelm me, in the hours of darkness I would wish him and his bastard son dead and summon up curses in my childish way. But in the hours of daylight, fearful that the Devil had heard me, I would pray to Saint Brynach, our parish saint for forgiveness.

All too soon, youth pulsed into life and talk of marriage drifted into the air. Many times, she of the pale skin and dancing eyes – was Mary her name? - had taunted me behind her joking talk as we walked across the fields after early Sunday Mass. She would let me kiss her and then laughing, always teasing. In spite of her bright face and tempting body, deep in my heart I knew she would never be the mother of my children.

Early one sunny morning we bade each other adieu, uttering false words of undying love as I turned my horse to the path that led to the River Wye and the old Roman road that would take me to Hereford and on to distant London. Only my mother shed a farewell tear and feared for my life, but my future and my stars beckoned.

Safety lay in numbers, so I travelled to London with a group of friends, youths from the village, each eager to push his horse to the limit every day. We looked like the plain country fellows we were, well and cleanly apparelled with leather jerkins under our gowns, but we knew to arm ourselves with swords and daggers, ready to counter any gangs of robbers that saw us as rich pickings. We made good progress without incident, but even when we first glimpsed London in the distance, danger still lurked along the Oxford Road. Soon the City walls and spires took shape and we urged our horses onwards, tired as they were after four days of constant travel.

Foul smells from the pits and troughs greeted us, and for a fleeting moment, I thought of the sweet scented honeysuckle that grew in profusion in the place of my birth. Then as if welcoming us to the great city, a rotting body swinging high from a gallows beside the way, brought me back to the place I now found myself. His stinking corpse proclaimed the fate of a felon. I still remember the sight of his staring eyes and protruding tongue; it made my horse stumble and my friends laugh.

We finally crossed Holborn Bridge and passed through the old New Gate with its unbroken line of timber framed houses standing like sentinels on either side. For my companions, their journey had ended; for me, mine had just begun.

I lay first at my Uncle John Aubrey's house near Mincing Lane, not far from the Clothworkers' Hall, a cramped and noisy place with his workshop that gave onto the street, above which were rooms where he and his wife Joan slept and a garret. The contrast between the dark narrow streets with their houses leaning towards each other at each successive storey as if trying to encroach on his neighbour's space and that of my father's manor house in midst of the endless green fields of Llanfrynach, I determined not to heed. I knew the discomfort and dark smells were but a stepping stone ~~ '

One day I awoke to the sound of . . . great Henry Tudor's son, King Henry, the eighth of that name had died – of the French pox - as rumour quickly explained. I remember my uncle saying to me in Welsh, we always spoke together in Welsh, especially when what we said needed to be hidden from our listeners,

'There'll be trouble aplenty now the boy king is come to the throne. Edward's not long for this world and there's only the old King's two daughters to follow him. I call 'chalk' one, and 'cheese' the other,' he said and then looked quickly around him in case he had been overheard.

As if to presage the shedding of much blood, neighbours told us of a most bizarre happening. King Hal's body was moved from his house at Westminster they call Whytehall, to lie in state at Syon House in Isleworth. The next morning, to their horror, the guards found the lid of the coffin open and a pack of dogs licking up the remains of the royal corpse. I knew not whether to believe the story, but nevertheless said an extra prayer for his soul that night.

Within days after his funeral, London became awash with excitement and nothing would keep me from joining the crowds along the route through the City to Westminster Abbey all agog to cheer the young Prince Edward on the day of his coronation.

The boy's uncle, Edward Seymour the Earl of Hertford, looked to dominate the procession of worthies resplendent in their red gowns. It seemed as if it was he who was about to be crowned, not the pale sickly child sitting uncomfortably beside him. The boy looked younger than his nine years. Even the Spaniard who flung himself down a rope suspended from St Paul's steeple to the cheers of the crowds who had lined the route, failed to produce any joy in his demeanour.

As my uncle predicted, Edward Seymour was given the title of Protector and made Duke of Somerset. He at once began building a magnificent palace for himself on the Strand, with gardens down to the Thames, first demolishing the houses of five bishops and numerous church grounds - to the despair of their hapless parishioners.

Almost immediately, statues and other images associated with Catholic ritual were removed from all parish churches and destroyed, and jewels and plate seized. The boy King had decreed that such familiar and comforting objects of worship were unwanted symbols of Popery. When I protested at this desecration, my Uncle John advised me to keep my peace and say my prayers as I had always done.

'Never fear, the Day of Judgement will come all too soon – too quickly for some when they blow against the wind.' He lowered his voice. 'You want to prosper in ways that God gives you breath in your body, do you not?' I nodded, thinking of my half-brother Richard enjoying the land that should have been mine.

'Then I advise you, when the wind changes as it must surely do again, be like the willow, not the oak, and so care for your earthly life first. Follow my precept, and you will bequeath riches unto your sons, and to their sons – for ever.'

This I determined to do, vowing that with the wealth I made, I would purchase my own land and be the lord of my own manor. So Mammon won over God and London embraced me.

2. Paths to Prosperity

The capital was bursting with opportunities that brought wealth for those with influence and initiative, particularly in the cloth trade. Sir Thomas Gresham[1], a merchant's son, shipped vast cargoes of material to Italian merchants in Antwerp in exchange for Italian silk and waxed fat from that dealing and his many other interests, enterprises that attracted profits like rats to rubbish.

People were happy to part with their money to purchase cloth to be made up into garments for themselves, their wives and their servants - courtiers and men of consequence and merchants of all ranks. The richest naturally chose the best they could find, and adorned their clothes with all manner of embroidery and brooches and rings to display their wealth.

I soon learnt all this because my Uncle John made his living as a clothworker. He and many others like him, such as his friend Richard Staper[2] another clothworker, were growing rich on cloth and cloth making and finishing.

I determined to follow their stars.

One day, James Peel a Salter[3], another friend of my uncle's, told me he could use the services of a strong and honest youth. I was happy to earn a penny or two when and where possible. Both men worked me hard and long. But I minded not, for they made it possible for me to make the acquaintance of men who would be useful to me, and they paid me when they could.

'Fight for every penny that's rightly yours,' my uncle would mutter, as he thrust a coin or two into my hand, 'there's rogues abroad aplenty.' Throughout my life, I endeavoured to follow my uncle's precept and example without question. So in those early years in London, I earned what I could; I listened and observed much.

His young wife, Mistress Joan, a plump woman in contrast to her husband, showed me great kindness and would take my side in the course of family quarrels that often erupted between my sister and me at that time. My sister Joan had also come to London after marrying William Taylor, a thin man with watery eyes, whom I detested. He once hinted that my mother had given my father good reason to leave her and for this besmirching of her character I would have ended his life there and then, had not my sister intervened. For her sake, I stayed my knife.

Even so, she always took our father's side when the subject of *ein tad* – our father - arose. That would make me angry, and we would shout - *yn Nshymraeg* - and Mistress Joan, whose Welsh was limited, would calm me down with a soft word and a gentle smile. I never forgot her sympathy and understanding in those early days. After her husband's death, and as I saw mine soon approaching, in my will I left her a mourning gown of black cloth.

I never forgot – or forgave – my father's injustice to me. Stories filtered into London that my half-brother's profligate ways were of great concern to my father. I could not help but smile when I contrasted Richard's failings with my own growing prosperity, forgetting for that moment the sin of Pride, which always reminded me of my Cousin Doctor William Aubrey[4], a kinsman who came to play such an important role in my life.

It soon became apparent that a life of a clothworker was sometimes fraught with many difficulties. My uncle often had trouble getting money owed to him by courtiers and new arrivals who all too often fell out of favour and into financial embarrassment.

I remember he took Thomas Morgan Aubrey to court because he failed to pay him for three yards of fine blue cloth at ten shillings a yard, two yards of velvet at twenty shillings a yard, an expensive gelding, and 3s-4d in money. It mattered not to him that Thomas was a kinsman, that his customer had been banished from Court and could not or would not pay him, or that the man had simply fallen on hard and difficult times.

Not as hard and difficult though, as those who did protest in a loud voice against the official restoration of Catholic ritual when King Henry's elder daughter the Lady Mary eventually came to the throne. My uncle learnt much of what took place in the interim after the boy King Edward died from a customer, a fervent but secret admirer of the Benedictine monk John Feckenham. Both he and my uncle despaired of the tangled web of deceit and cruelty that was set in train after the ailing King Edward eventually went to his Maker.

In order to prevent the Catholic Lady Mary from succeeding him, the Duke of Northumberland and Henry Grey Duke of Suffolk proclaimed the young Lady Jane Grey, Queen. This was contrary to old King Henry's wishes, but the two men seized the opportunity to promote their power and influence. The Lady Jane was a grand-daughter of Mary Tudor and a devoted Protestant whose parents had just married her to the Duke of Northumberland's son Lord Guildford Dudley – against her wishes.

As Queen Jane, she was received into the Tower with a great company of lords and nobles to a firing of guns and a blowing of trumpets while two heralds went abroad declaring that the Lady Mary was unlawfully begotten. A young man who spoke for the Lady Mary was promptly arrested, put in the pillory and had both his ears cut off.

Nine days after Queen Jane's coronation, the Lady Mary and her followers asserted her right to succeed King Edward as her father had intended, with the result that we saw much shedding of the plotters' blood.

The poor young Jane Grey, forced to be Queen and the most innocent of the flies caught in the web of the Dukes' intrigue, returned to the Tower, this time as a prisoner awaiting execution. John Feckenham went to her prison cell to comfort her and remained to help her prepare for death. He urged her to convert to Catholicism, but she thanked him for his kindness saying, 'The faith of the church must be tried by God's word, and not God's word by the church, and the same goes for my faith.'

The next day Jane saw her husband's carcase thrown into a cart and his head in a cloth while under her window, on the green against the White Tower, they prepared the platform for her execution.

John Feckenham gently helped her mount the scaffold. She asked him if she should say the psalm *Miserere mei Deus* and when he said 'Yea', she knelt down and recited it in English in the most devout of manner. Then the executioner knelt down and asked her forgiveness which she gave most willingly. Then she said, 'I pray you dispatch me quickly.' With her eyes covered, one of the by-standers guided her to the block. She laid her head down upon it and said, 'Lord, into thy hands I commend my spirit.'

The executioner killed her with one blow and held up her head saying, 'So perish all the Queen's enemies! Behold the head of a traitor!'

So with the Lady Mary as Queen, we followed all the old familiar Catholic rituals, hearing the Mass in Latin and receiving not the bread and wine per se, but once again believing it to be in fact, the flesh and blood of Christ.

Each day my uncle, with his lean and knowing look, would regale us with the latest hangings and burnings of those who protested against the old manner of worshipping God. Edward Bonner, the Bishop of London seemed to welcome any opportunity of setting fire to a person – man or woman - whose belief in the Reformed Church overcame all considerations of the dreadful fate that awaited them.

I knew from my uncle that John Feckenham in contrast, showed great mildness to the heretics, many of whom he converted, and some he saved from the stake. In my secret thoughts, I considered it very unlikely that our Almighty God would object to hearing the Mass being said in Latin or being worshipped in a church adorned with statues. As for the transubstantiation of the sacred bread and wine, I kept those thoughts to myself.

Such martyrs, for that was what the protesters became, paid for their adherence to the Reformed Church in agonising terror. They said that when John Rogers, the vicar of St Sepulchre's was burned at the stake, he washed his hands in the flames as though it had been in cold water. He did not. I happened to be at Smithfield with the crowd that had gathered there on that cold February day to witness the event and saw and smelt the fire greedily licking and consuming his flesh. His piercing screams rang in my ears for days afterwards – nay, weeks.

But I digress from my account relating to the paths I took to earn the riches that God in His wisdom favoured me to enjoy. In time, it became increasingly apparent that a clothworker not only had difficulty getting the money owed to him, but also his customers of all rank and estate suffered limitations and restrictions as to what they could wear. There were countless decrees pertaining to dress that had to be strictly adhered to, on pain of punishment. Colours and cloth were naturally expected to indicate one's rank and station. Even the size of ruffs and lengths of cloaks were officially restricted.

Nevertheless, there was good money to be made by turning a blind eye, as so many did, and giving a customer the colour of the cloth or the size of the ruff he wanted.

But I still had needs become an apprentice as custom demanded. At the end of the seven years, I would become a Freeman and a Citizen of London and vote in civic elections. Then, I could become an Alderman and even Lord Mayor. Endless possibilities lay on the horizon for men of ambition of which I saw myself as one, and not a sin to be such, neither.

I would become a Salter.

For such I reasoned: What man who can live without salt? Who can live without his salted beef in winter time, or his salted fish on fast days? What poor sailor can survive months at sea without his salted fish and biscuit? At my village school we learned that the Romans who once occupied these islands even paid their soldiers in salt; now I knew that the substance was a world-wide commodity whose trade continued even in time of war. Salt was essential in order to preserve food and thus sustain life, and those who controlled the market grew rich in the process.

The sale of salt and its distribution lay in the hands of the City Company that dated all the way back to 1394. King Richard II accorded a licence to found a Fraternity composed entirely of those who followed the trade of Salter and imposed strict rules on their activities. They were forbidden to withhold supplies until demand increased the price, they were never to discuss the guild's business in public, or to conduct themselves indecorously at meetings. Punishment for such misdemeanours meant being beaten, fined or put in the pillory.[5] I could see none of this to object to, especially when such an honourable guild could open more doors to my prosperity as it had done to so many before me. Nearly a hundred years ago, in 1487, Sir William Littlesbury had been a merchant of the staple and then became a member of the early Fraternity of Salters – and Lord Mayor of London.

Such were the dreams that came to be the spurs to my ambition. So, with my uncle's blessing, I became bound for the statutory seven years to James Peel.

On Thursday 19 December 1560, three years into the reign of Queen Elizabeth, the Court of Aldermen convened and agreed that I should be received into the Company of the Salters, paying to the Chamberlain, 20 shillings for the privilege.

Difficult as it was for me to find the money, it was worth every penny.

---

1. Sir Thomas Gresham (1519-1579), financier and international money market operator; heavily involved in the cloth trade; ambassador to the Netherlands; from his own wealth, founded the Royal Exchange.
2. Richard Staper Alderman and Master Clothworker, of Aldersgate, d. 30 June 1608. He is described on his monument in St Helen's Bishopsgate as 'the greatest merchant in his tyme, the chiefest actor in discovery of the trades of Turkey and East India.'
3. James Peel Salter of Christ Church Newgate d. 30 December 1585. Clerk of the Hospital.
4. Dr William Aubrey (c1529-1595) D.C.L., fellow of Jesus College, Regius Professor of Civil Law, a Master in Chancery and a Master of Requests, Vicar-general to Archbishop of Canterbury, ambassador in France, M.P. for Carmarthen, Brecknock, etc.
5. See Appendix E.

3. The Sign of the Black Swan

S oon my uncle advised me to look for a suitable wife, for times had changed and Queen Elizabeth had succeeded her sister Mary and now sat securely on the throne of England.

Never was a Monarch more beloved than she. I was truly privileged to see her riding through the crowded streets in a public procession to the Tower, smiling and gracious and clad in purple velvet and with a scarf about her neck. People who could remember, saw in her a likeness to her father when young. Children on the way welcomed her with speeches, others played the regals and sang while trumpets rang out and the sound of guns noised through it all, such as never heard before. The whole of London sighed in relief and rejoiced at the coming of such mildness and majesty.

My uncle had become friendly with John Vaux, a Warden of the Merchant Taylors' Company who recommended his sister as a possible

Robert Vaux of Cumberland =
    |
1. Francis Vaux =
        |
        Issue

2. John Vaux Citizen & Merchant Taylor (d.c1604)
  = Alice Barrister (d.c1614)
        |
        Issue

3. Joan Vaux (d.1614)
  = 1) Simon Holman of Stratton, Cornwall
        |
      1. Nicholas Holman of Buckland Brewer, Devon

  = 2) Morgan Aubrey of London (c1527-1608)
        |
      1. Katherine Aubrey (1572-1617)
      2. Samuel Aubrey (1580-1645)

choice. I had long since ceased thinking of my first love, she of the pale skin and dancing eyes.

Some deplore the practice of men having their wives chosen for them but in my case, the moment Joan Vaux and I looked at each other, we both felt that Providence, or God, had put us together. I knew at once she was the wife I wanted and I vowed I would never forsake her as my father had my mother.

Joan was a widow, and had money - always a useful addition to a pretty face and lusty figure. She needed a husband and I needed a wife. Besides, she had given her first husband a son and that was a good omen as well. Joan had lived for a time in Cornwall of which she had fond memories, although she rarely mentioned her first husband, Simon Holman of Stratton. Of young Nicholas, she never spoke.

The Vauxs came from Cumberland, far away to the north and it was not long before they had successfully established themselves in London. Her brother John lived in a large house near the north end of London Bridge in the parish of St Magnus the Martyr, among other wealthy citizens and prosperous merchants like Mercers and Haberdashers and other Merchant Taylors. He also possessed estates outside London, in Middlesex and Hertfordshire, an example I was now even more keen to follow.

Joan and I moved into St Mary Abchurch parish, in the east side of the city, not far from Bread Street, where we Salters held our meetings in the newly built Salters' Hall, the old one having been totally destroyed by fire in 1539. Neither was Joan too far from her brother's family in the parish of St Magnus the Martyr.

She chose the place we were to live in for the rest of our lives together. The timber framed house boasted a shop that opened onto the street, for taking the advice of my uncle and Mr Staper – and with the help of my wife's money – I began buying and selling (at a good profit) cloth of whatever quality of I could buy. Behind the shop was a stockroom, that lead into a kitchen, with chambers and a garret above, and a cellar below. It even boasted a privy. The house stood out from the other dwellings on the south side of Candlewick Street, which I believe is now called Cannon Street.

Most of our neighbours were Welsh and many had grown rich as drapers and cloth merchants – some were old friends and colleagues. So we lived in the midst of useful acquaintances, but none lived in a house quite like ours. You could see the distinctive pattern of our abode the moment you set foot in the street.

Our Black Swan is really like what Juvenal would call a rare bird,' Joan observed with a smile. 'No other Black Swan in London meets ours for its patterning.'

I was secretly proud of the fact that Joan could read and understand Latin, the language I knew so well from my school days. We were taught in Latin, the rules of Latin grammar were beaten into us, and we were even forced to speak it among ourselves, in the belief that nothing was more profitable to a young man than to speak the language of the great Caesars.

Joan could quote long passages from Juvenal, her favourite Roman poet and to remind her that she was only a weak woman, I would let forth a stream of Welsh - of which she was completely ignorant - and claimed they were the words of my favourite bard. She knew no different, but laughingly teased me, saying I was just reciting my line of ancestors, a feat we Welsh can do so easily. That reminded me of my father and my mood changed, but Joan would always kiss me happy again.

So I moved from my Uncle John's house and settled into married life at the Sign of the Black Swan where business soon grew. Joan ran the household with great efficiency and chose our servants well, particularly Joan Sheffell, a comely wench with a smiling face under a mop of dark curls who would do anything for her mistress. Joan taught her what plants and herbs would cure what ailments, and how to malt and brew.

She would tell her to put on her best linen apron and take her to Cheap to buy vegetables and eggs and cheese or wander up to the Leadenhall market for meat. Joan knew how much a fat, sweet salmon pleased me, so she and Sheffell would take a walk to Old Fish Street down near the river where they could be assured that the fish came straight from the Thames. A bright lass, Sheffell quickly learned where to shop for our necessaries and get the best value for her pennies.

This left Joan time to walk and ride and visit our friends and relations when so inclined, but most of all, she understood and enjoyed discussing with me, matters to do with money. As a result I continued to prosper and of course I had to pay the unwelcome Subsidy Tax on my land and goods but every night I thanked God for sending me such a wife. I lacked only one blessing and that was a son but at last to my joy, in 1562, Joan was with child and at that, my cup runneth over.

From time to time clouds would darken our horizon as we heard the dreaded news of a neighbour falling prey to the sweating sickness. We would notice the signs of impending disaster, when people no longer put their rubbish into the pits outside the City gates for the rakers to cart it away, but dumped their filth in the streets.

The smell rose like an evil omen. Bonfires were ordered to be lit three times a week, and blue crosses were put on all houses whose inhabitants had fallen victim to the disease. People blamed the state of the heavens but Joan insisted the servants scrub out the house every day, turn and clean the rushes, sprinkle them with her favourite lavender spike and took no notice of their grumbling.

That year Cousin William gave me the Court news that the Queen had the smallpox. Joan and I immediately went to St Mary Abchurch and prayed for her recovery. As well, we both asked God to care for the child in Joan's womb. The Queen survived, and so did Joan who soon after was delivered of a girl child. We called her Marjorie and on the twenty-fifth of May in the year of Our Lord 1563, we took her to be baptised at St Mary Abchurch.

All that year, people around us died like flies. They say the English soldiers at Le Havre caught the plague and brought it back to London. A quarter of the population perished, rich and poor alike. Theatres were closed and anyone who could, left London, and took their boxes of medicines and perfumes to ward off the stench of the dead and dying. Joan begged me to leave London and stay with her brother John. He had taken his family to Bedfordshire where he had recently bought another estate, this one near a field grimly called Gallows Close, but I refused. I knew the worst was over - or so I thought.

Little Marjorie gave us great joy and I can still hear her gurgle with delight when Joan cradled her. Sheffell adored her almost as much as we did and played with her as often as her duties allowed. Marjorie had started lisping her first strings of words when disaster struck.

In the summer of 1565, the sun beat down for days on end. The servants had slackened off with their work, but Sheffell took her basket as usual and went to the market at Newgate to buy some fresh meat. The next day, she looked unwell. Joan told her to take to her bed, but she refused and instead played her usual games with Marjorie.

When Sheffell showed evidence of the fever, Joan tended her every day and made her drink bruised roots of the white garden lily boiled in wine but to no avail. Within the week our devoted servant was dead. John Cooke our kitchen boy howled in his grief and little Marjorie, not understanding what had happened, began to cry in sympathy. We buried our servant at St Mary Abchurch. Even Joan wept and declared she would never find her like again. After that, Joan would not let little Marjorie out of her sight. Now the child slept with us. We couldn't explain and she couldn't understand that Sheffell had gone to God.

Then our worst nightmares were realised. Marjorie grew listless, and we could feel her hot and see the sweat on her brow. We buried her at St Mary Abchurch three weeks after poor, faithful Sheffell and I watched through moist eyes, the shaking hand write on the page of burials in the Year of our Lord 1565 – under so many others –

'Marjorie the daughter of Morgan Aubrey buried the 15th June.'

I asked God why? What sins had I committed to deserve such a loss? But answer He gave me none.

We have a saying in Welsh, *'pawb á'i fys lle bo'i ddolur'* or 'everyone puts his finger where his pain is', so to help us get over our grief, Joan and I agreed that I should help the many orphans of freemen whose parents had died in the plague. So soon after little Marjorie's funeral, I went with my friends Miles Raven and Hugh Henley, who had also lost persons close to them in the plague, to the Guildhall. There the Orphans' Court appointed us as Guardians of a child whose father, a fellow Salter, had just died. We made a formal promise, signed the recognisance and put up £93 each as surety to safeguard the child's inheritance.

Joan and I busied ourselves as well as we could, but I noticed that Joan's eyes often had a haunted look and many times she went to St Mary Abchurch to pray. I turned my attention more and more to business as a salve for my grief, with the result that in 1568 I was assessed in the Subsidy Rolls as having personal property of land and goods worth £60 and was thus obliged to pay 60 shillings to the Crown. Joan halted my grumbling at having to pay more tax, as she always did, by sharply reminding me to count my blessings instead.

Soon I knew I would have one more to count when Joan came with child again. We named the boy William, not after my father but after my cousin, whose star was still in the ascendant. The moment I saw the wailing, puny baby and remembered Marjorie who seemed to smile the moment she came out of the womb, I knew he would not live beyond the year. Months later we watched the tiny coffin lowered into the ground at St Mary Abchurch. Then came another boy, a second William, but he too died while still in his swaddling clothes.

When little Kate came into our lives, it was another matter. I knew she had a mind of her own, the moment I held her in my arms, but I loved her nevertheless, disappointed as I was, that she was only a girl.

Nine years later in 1580, when I had all but given up hope of ever siring a son and heir, my prayers were answered. Joan came with child again and this time to our joy, she bore a son. She insisted on naming him after Samuel the boy who heeded God's call after twice before being summoned.

I knew I was blessed. I had high hopes for him.

4. Gloriana's 'Little Doctor'

Imust now needs acknowledge my Cousin Dr William Aubrey, whose life came to be so closely bound up with mine, and whose name I have heretofore mentioned. When we were boys, before my Uncle Thomas sent him off to Christ's College in Brecknock town, he would antagonise me, then we would quarrel and often come to blows. I was two years older than he, but William always enjoyed sneering and taunting me in that arrogant way he had. It hurt me that my father would hold him up as a paragon of virtue, particularly when he cast veiled aspersions concerning my mother – which at the time I did not understand.

'I know William better! He's a youth what thinks highly of himself – he's proud!! And Pride is one of the seven deadly sins!,' I once angrily retorted to my father in defence of myself and of I knew not what. For that rudeness, he gave me a whipping and sent me to bed hungry.

When William was about fourteen, my Uncle Thomas sent him away to the University of Oxford and I was glad to see the last of him. He studied Civil Law with such earnest diligence, that he was elected into the Fellowship of All Souls College and Jesus and thereafter, at the age of twenty-five years, attained the degree of Doctor of the Civil Law and glorified in his appointment as Principal of New Hall, Oxford.

Even although we had both grown to man's estate, William tended to patronise me still in those early days in London, when his fame for learning and knowledge was already spread far abroad. He had married Wilgiford, a proud young woman, the daughter of John Williams of Tainton in the county of Oxford who soon did her duty to him by giving him a son and heir, a fact she frequently reminded us when we met.

I suppose he now had some reason to be proud, considering his position and whom his benefactor was, our kinsman Henry Herbert the Earl of Pembroke, one of the richest peers in the realm. The Earl restored Cardiff castle and entertained there lavishly, Cousin William being among his honoured guests. It was he who secured Cousin William as a Member of Parliament for Brecknock and then Carmarthen. I had no patron, nevertheless I forgave William his early antagonism to me and put it down to childish foolishness on his part.

By the time I had established myself, William's attitude towards me softened, particularly when I became a Freeman of the Salters' Guild and started making good money.

In spite of his stern look and searching eyes, William knew how to make himself agreeable when circumstances dictated, like many others at Court. On becoming Professor of Civil Laws, Queen Mary appointed him to a readership in Common Law, and when she declared war on the French, William went to France with Pembroke's expeditionary force as Judge Advocate of the Queen's armies at St. Quentin in France.

After we lost possession of Calais, he told me he persuaded Her Majesty to console herself with the thought, that rather than it being a disaster, she could only benefit from the defeat. Had it remained in English hands, the French would always covet the town and bring forces to attack it, which Her Majesty would have to defend with men and arms.

Years later, William ingratiated himself - of necessity, I must admit - into the new Queen's good graces when she came to the throne after Queen Mary died. He kept aloof from Court intrigue, but made himself useful to Sir William Cecil the Queen's Secretary, Sir Francis Walsingham Secretary of State and hence to Queen Elizabeth herself. He loved to boast that she was wont to call him 'Her Little Doctor'. I smiled to myself when I first heard him proudly announce this proof of his influence at Court, remembering the whipping I'd received at the hands of my father.

His wife Wilgiford never failed to remind us how much the good Queen loved him and I began to realise that I had fallen prey to one of the seven deadly sins myself - Envy. I remembered our Welsh proverb, 'cenfigen a ladd ei pherchennog' or 'envy destroys its possessor', so I said an extra prayer that night as a penance and resolved to heed my sinful thoughts, in case some ill should befall me because of them.

I saw my Cousin William less and less often as he became involved in Court affairs and Church politics. He now devoted himself to his practice in the Prerogative and Ecclesiastical Courts as Master in Chancery and to Wilgiford's delight, Queen Elizabeth appointed William Vicar-General to the next Archbishop of Canterbury, Edmund Grindal. The new Archbishop had taken it into his head to be a new broom and reform the spiritual Courts, and commissioned a series of reports to outline the current failings of the Church.

In spite of our concerns, William threw himself into the project with his usual enthusiasm and Wilgiford boasted to us that his series of recommendations numbered fifty-five paragraphs and was quite the longest.

We all knew there was plenty that needed attention, but Joan and I considered this to be a dangerous course of action with serious consequences, not only for William, but for me. He had become very important in my life, introducing me to influential people at Court and without boasting overly much, I knew I was the richest man in our parish.

Of course many of Grindal's ideas incurred the wrath of some influential prelates and the Archbishop fell out of favour with Her Majesty who had him put under house arrest. This naturally worried Wilgiford, who thought that the Queen might include William in her displeasure, but he remained in her good graces and continued in his position as Vicar-General to the next Archbishop of Canterbury, John Whitgift.

All of these Court and Church intrigues paled into insignificance compared with the drama of the woman who for most of her life attracted blood and betrayal, death and murder like bees to honey. I refer of course to Mary who became Queen of the Scots when only five days old and Queen of France when she married François the Second. She was now Queen Regnant of Scotland, eyeing the throne of England.

William was one of the Commissioners at her trial, as was his benefactor the Earl of Pembroke. Wilgiford confided in Joan that the Queen had always been against the idea of executing an anointed sovereign, and she finally agreed to sign her cousin's death certificate only with great reluctance. In spite of the fact that the woman had instigated plots against our Queen and was a Catholic to boot, William wanted to save her life and secretly regretted the sorry outcome.

William did me the honour of allowing me to make the acquaintance of Sir James Croft, another Commissioner of Mary's trial. I found him a reserved man with penetrating eyes, unwilling to reveal his true thoughts. He had been a great favourite of Her Majesty ever since they were both implicated - falsely of course - in Wyatt's Rebellion back in 1554 and spent some time in the Tower. Soon after her coronation, and because of his loyalty to Her Majesty during those difficult days when her Catholic sister sat on the throne, Queen Elizabeth made Sir James Lord Deputy of Ireland and Comptroller of the Royal Household. As well, she granted him extensive tracts of land in Herefordshire.

Cousin William also acquired extensive estates in Brecknockshire and Herefordshire, some by royal grant and some by purchase. When he could, he would leave Wilgiford and his children in London to visit them to make merry with his friends. I followed his acquisitions with interest and was even more determined to emulate him in this respect.

What man does not dream and plan the best for his son and heir, to have the means and the foresight to hand on to him and to future generations a valuable and lasting inheritance? I believed that the destiny of my son Samuel – and his sons - would lie in Herefordshire.

I can still smell its clean air and see the splashes of pink and red apple blossom even along the hedgerows and remember the taste of cider in my throat. Such a country, not far from the place of my birth promised a different kind of riches to those who owned it, with its sweet soil, abundant apples and corn and hops and the cattle that people boasted were the best in the land.

I set my heart on acquiring property in Herefordshire.

5. *A Night with Dr Dee*

Joan had a difficult time at his birth, but Samuel proved to be a healthy enough baby and only cried when he was hungry, so I was in no hurry to have him baptised. I could not believe that a child who died without baptism would be a firebrand of Hell and damned for eternity, in spite of what the Vicar of Ashford in Kent, declared. His utterances had taken a fashionable hold in London but to me, the whole business amounted to a superstitious ritual. Joan of course believed otherwise, and when I said so, her haunted look brought back memories of our other two sons and little Marjorie's smile flashed into my mind's eye. So at the first opportunity, Joan and I took our son and heir to St Mary Abchurch to be baptised and named Samuel Aubrey.

It had been my destiny to suffer humiliation at the hands of my father, when he renounced my mother on a trumped up charge of infidelity and disowned me, his rightful heir. So as soon as Samuel looked to thrive, I determined to have his horoscope cast. I wanted to know what attributes the boy should develop and which failings of character, if any, he should overcome – in short, what the future held for him.

Dr John Dee[1], the Queen's Astrologer-Royal and a kinsman, was gracious, as always, to discuss the matter with me when I visited his home at Mortlake on the river, a few miles upstream of London, not far from Sir Francis Walsingham's house at Barnes. Cousin William, his great friend, had effected our introduction.

His property contained laboratories and large panelled rooms for the assistants whom Dr Dee usually had living there. The vast chambers housed his library of scientific, mathematical and medical books and manuscripts, many of which he had managed to salvage after the dissolution of the monasteries. His devotion to science and alchemy and my interest as a Salter in the mixing of salt with other substances such as soap and dyes, commodities that always brought a good profit, ensured our friendship.

Dr Dee had lectured on mathematics at the College of Rheims and at Oxford and had penned an introduction to the first English edition of Euclid. He long had been a great favourite of the Queen, herself a scholar of no mean repute, ever since she had honoured him by inviting him to choose an auspicious date for her coronation. He further endeared himself to Gloriana when he told her that America had not been discovered first by Christopher Columbus, but by the eleventh century Welsh prince, Madoc, a distant ancestor of our Queen which of course proved that the New World rightly belonged to England.

He had survived many perils. One such, that he remembered even after a quarter of a century, was his imprisonment at Hampton Court on a trumped up charge of supposedly trying to destroy Queen Mary by 'enchantments'. He had been acquitted of treason, only to find himself in the hands of Bishop Bonner, the zealous burner of heretics, who examined him at length on religious and other matters.

'I was prisoner long, and bedfellow with Bartlet Greene, who was burnt.' Nothing more would he say on the subject, but turned to more promising matters such as his advice that he had been asked to give on the next exploration to North America.

His library was said to be the largest in all of Europe and the number of books he owned was a sight to behold. It never ceased to astound me whenever I visited him. I knew him to be one of Europe's greatest mathematicians and he laughed when I once asked him if he knew the exact number of volumes he possessed. He uttered a complicated mathematical formula and told me with a smile that the answer was exactly four thousand. I knew not whether to believe him, but he filled my glass with perry, knowing how much I enjoyed his pear cider, and turned our discussion to more immediate matters.

Always a man of kindness and generosity, that night he agreed to cast Samuel's horoscope. So after his lovely young wife Jane had retired, we talked far into the small hours, at first discoursing on his many experiments with spells and angelology and his progress in turning base metal into gold.

'Ah, gold! Sometimes I think it is to be found only at the end of the rainbow! Or even at the end of one's life!'

With that unanswerable thought, I watched him in silence as he dipped his pen into the ink and carefully marked the symbols of the zodiac onto the circle according to the exact moment that Samuel had uttered his first cry in this world. For a long time I heard only the scratch of the writing on the parchment.

At last he looked up and said, 'From the aspects of the planets, I can see a fortunate life and a fruitful marriage ahead. However, with the Moon in the Sextile Saturn, he may experience some future peril that he will need fortitude to overcome.'

Dr Dee refused to elaborate on this cloud that hovered over an otherwise happy divination. I assured him that it was enough to know that with diligence on the boy's part, he would be fit to enter one of the City livery companies. He could do this by right of patrimony, unlike my entry into the Mystery of the Salters, which had been by redemption.

My host nodded politely as my thoughts slipped easily into words, helped by the power of his pear cider.

'With such an auspicious horoscope, Samuel could become an Alderman of the City or even Lord Mayor of London!' Dr Dee filled our glasses.

'One thing he never will be, and that is a Welsh farmer like my brother! – God rest his soul.'

We had learned of Hopkin's death soon after Samuel's baptism. He never wanted to leave Glamorganshire, he was happy to stay on his farm which prospered in spite of suffering the uncertainties of the seasons. Like my sister, he always took my father's side and for this I hated him, but now he was dead and I was sorry for the cruel words I had said to him in my anger. But thoughts of my father still hurt when I let them enter my head. Now I learnt that Hopkin had named me the executor of his will.

Joan thought I should travel all the way to Llangwig and deal with his estate, but I knew that returning to Wales would bring back too many memories of an unhappy childhood and my wronged mother. Besides, I could not bear to leave little Samuel and I had no use for kyne or oxen or barley - only money and property, although I was thankful for the little of those he left me, and these I would leave to Samuel. When I declined to be his executor, as Hopkin suspected I would, my sister Joan Taylor and her husband took over the task.

'You show great wisdom Mr Aubrey. For while the soil yields rich harvests, who can tell precisely when the icy winds will abate and the winter snow melt? Only the birds of the air, I believe.' He refreshed our goblets. 'Even so, it takes time for even a rich harvest to turn into gold. You would do better to follow in the wake our friend Sir Thomas.'

Again through Cousin William, I had made the acquaintance of Sir

Thomas Gresham[2] and had early on resolved to offer my humble service to this most famous merchant and international financier and so emulate his success. In fact, he came to play no small part in my life, and at the time, the name of this paragon of fiscal virtue was on everyone's lips.

Older than I by about ten years, he entered this world as the second son of Sir Richard Gresham, a mercer. After attending Gonville Collage Cambridge, he was apprenticed to his Uncle Sir John Gresham and then admitted to the Mercers' Company, after which his star steadily rose.

A man of imposing stature, he looked down at me at our first meeting, his dark eyes assessing the world under thick brows, and his long ragged beard and short neck all but hiding his narrow ruff. He graciously hinted that he might be ready to accept a sum of money from me and so be included in his latest trading enterprise. From that moment, I knew that my stars were in the ascendancy – and so were those of my son and heir.

Joan believed that he saw the world only in terms of bad money driving out good, nevertheless, after our meeting I sent him a dozen of quails and although Joan demurred at such extravagance, we were rewarded with an invitation to be present when Her Majesty opened the Royal Exchange. Sir Thomas had built this wonderful edifice at his own cost, after clearing eighty houses in Cornhill, near the Stocks market.

From the debris rose a magnificent tall classical building, all of four storeys high, adorned with stone grasshoppers and with covered arcades built around a courtyard. On the roof, we could see a huge, gilded grasshopper, the emblem of bankers that Sir Thomas had made his own. A great bell-tower looked down on the crowds milling below: merchants and traders, making their way to the haberdashers, drapers, goldsmiths, glass-sellers, milliners, wigmakers and drapers selling their wares in the hundred or so chambers above the arcades. We all knew that such a magnificent exchange meant that London now surpassed Venice and Antwerp for the trading of commodities.

Sir Thomas had made himself indispensable to Her Majesty as her Royal Agent in the Netherlands so, on the twenty-third day of January in the year of Our Lord 1571, she graciously consented to dine at his house in Bishopsgate and then officially open the building which she allowed him to call the Royal Exchange. Joan and I were among the earliest guests honoured to be present for the occasion.

I recounted the event to Dr Dee. 'Sir Thomas and the royal party arrived in great splendour to the cheering approval of the crowds. Had I not been present, I would not have believed what I later saw with mine own eyes. We all grew silent as Sir Thomas raised a golden goblet aloft to pledge the health of Her Majesty.

'He held it up for all to see and as he did so, we could see the jewels inlaid in the drinking cup. Truly, they danced in the sunlight. The goblet not only held the best of Rhenish wine, but also a precious stone worth £15,000 that had been crushed to powder.

'Sir Thomas drank the toast, the crowd roared, Her Majesty clapped her hands in delight and for days afterwards, London could talk of little else!'

'Would I had been there to witness such a scene!' said Dr Dee.

By now a new day had begun with a grey dawn. I expressed my gratitude and took my leave. Dr Dee had confirmed my decision to forego my brother's kine and oxen. More important, I now knew where Samuel's destiny lay and with God's blessing, his future would be assured.

Thereafter, I spent many hours of my day at the Royal Exchange, a focus for merchants like myself, meeting friends and enlarging my circle of acquaintances. Thus I prospered, heeding my Uncle John's advice and ensuring the outward show of my spiritual beliefs mirrored those of our good Queen and her advisers, and particularly those of my Cousin William, whose star was rising ever higher.

1. Dr John Dee (1527-1608), acclaimed geographer, astronomer and mathematician; scientific and medical consultant to Elizabeth I; studied and researched in the fields of astrology, alchemy, crystal divination and Rosicrucianism.

2. Sir Thomas Gresham (1519-1579), financier, became England's leading operator in the international money market and cloth trade; founded the Royal Exchange.

6. Kate

Once Samuel and Kate overcame their childish ailments and grew strong and sturdy, it was as though a new chapter had begun in our lives. Kate had grown up into a buxom lass with a handsome face, brown dancing eyes and a lively disposition. She was now taller than I and enjoyed teasing her younger brother, never letting him forget she was older than he by eight years. Joan taught her to read and write and she proved to be an apt pupil – quick to learn, but restless, not steady like her mother. Soon she could even understand a smattering of Latin and this she would flaunt to her young brother, making Samuel declare that if she could speak it, he wanted none of the silly language.

Kate in turn showed little interest in learning how to malt and brew and what plants and herbs cured what ailments. At times, nothing would induce her to obey me and I despaired of her. Those who know what it is to have an ungrateful and wilful daughter, will understand and sympathise with me.

Cousin William's wife Wilgiford had given him several children, who throve and grew up, all happily obedient to him, and I felt that surge of envy rise again whenever we met them. Only Joan could bring peace and harmony into the Sign of the Black Swan and in my heart, at times, I felt grateful.

I consoled myself with the thought that Kate was too young to understand the consequences of being a female with a headstrong disposition. There were examples aplenty with which to teach her. One such was another Kate, the sister of Jane Grey, the one time Queen whose brief reign of nine days ended in such an orgy of blood-letting.

That other Katherine had been married to Henry Herbert the Earl of Pembroke and Cousin William's benefactor, but later divorced him. Knowing something of her character from Cousin William, the later sequence of events and their outcome did not surprise us.

The girl became enamoured of Edward Seymour, Earl of Hertford and secretly, without the Queen's permission, married him. As a result, she incurred Her Majesty's wrath and was sent to the Tower where she gave birth to a son. Court intrigue was rife and Cousin William was appointed to be a member of Archbishop Parker's commission to deliberate on the case, the Queen being still a virgin and Katherine Grey being a great-niece of old King Henry and according to his will, next in line to the throne.

Then the silly girl gave birth to yet another son, making the matter of succession to the Queen even more important. Naturally William and his fellow Commissioners declared her marriage illegal, and Katherine was put under house arrest at Cockfield Hall in Suffolk where she died aged twenty-eight.

I often related Katherine Grey's story to my wife and daughter as a lesson, knowing as I did, so many of the details from Cousin William. But nothing would ever convince my daughter that her namesake got what she deserved. The little miss always burst into tears and ran from the room whenever I related this story to make her see some sense. It never helped that if Samuel was present, he would laugh and applaud the outcome.

Kate needed a husband and I determined to start searching for one. At last I found a man whom I considered to be eminently suitable. Francis Bevans came from Carmarthenshire, but more important than that, he had consolidated his position in the community there as a Justice of the Peace, and had just been appointed Chancellor of the diocese of Hereford.

Having such a son-in-law as Frank, as he was known to his intimates, would enhance my standing in the community and greatly increase my chances of leasing diocesan land there. His Bishop, Herbert Westfaling, had already acquired much property and had the distinction of being married to Anne Barlow, whose four sisters all married bishops. In addition, her uncle, Thomas Barlow, had at one time been chaplain to Queen Anne Boleyn. It augured well and I believed the stars were now urgently prompting me to acquire land in Herefordshire as Cousin William had done.

Frank seemed to be genuinely surprised at the sum I offered for Kate's dower and I suspected that he had little use for money, nor did he seem to be interested in worldly things. Still, my daughter's future would be secure and she had the right to the support from her husband's property for the rest of her life. He was fourteen years older than she, but he could tame her and teach her to be steady and obedient.

Instead of being pleased and grateful at my choosing such a suitable husband, Kate threw herself into a tantrum and swore she could never like him. 'He's dull and old! I'll never marry him!' she screamed. I sent her to bed hungry and told her she could return only when she learnt to obey her father.

Joan went and talked to her for a long time. Frank might have seen more years than she, but he was not disfigured and would make her a kind husband. She promised Kate we would visit her in Hereford whenever we could and reminded her that she would be living in a cleaner place, where the plague visited less frequently and less severely, away from the noise and smells of London. Finally, Joan made her see sense and Kate slowly lost her sulky look. So the banns were cried at St Mary Abchurch and in the Cathedral Church of Hereford.

The wedding day dawned, Joan helped her into her best gown and arranged her beautiful garland of rosemary and white Christmas roses. We left the Sign of the Black Swan just as the snow stopped falling and made our way to St Mary Abchurch. Kate married a smiling Frank Bevans on the morning of the fourth day of a freezing January in the year of Our Lord 1588.

The Sign of the Black Swan was strangely quiet after Kate left to live in Herefordshire, and I confessed to Joan in the darkness of one bitterly cold night that the house sorely lacked the warm sound of her voice and laughter. Joan could only weep in my arms.

Samuel was now at school, where we expected him to learn grammar, geometry, arithmetic, music, the rudiments of Greek and of course be fluent in Latin. He exhibited a pleasing competence in music, but as for the rest, not even frequent beatings by his masters produced any noticeable improvement in his grasp of these subjects.

Nevertheless, I comforted myself with remembering the boy's horoscope, even when he confessed to his mother that he was spending most of his time in school hours playing dice.

At Joan's insistence, I did not punish him for succumbing to such a temptation, but simply reminded him how quickly his sister had learned her lessons and how easily she had acquired a knowledge of Latin. He could only mumble his excuses without meeting my eye.

Eventually we heard that Kate was with child. That day, the servant of one of our neighbours in Candlewick Street fell ill and we knew the plague would soon be upon us again. Immediately Joan insisted we take

Samuel and the servants and go to Hereford and stay there for Kate's lying-in, away from the worst of the pestilence. This time I agreed, for there were men to meet and properties to be inspected in Herefordshire. I thanked God I did, for the plague took its toll and some 18,000 people perished in the inner parishes of London alone.

The girl had a difficult time giving birth in spite of the midwife's charms and prayers, but at last she produced a healthy baby. She wanted to call him William, I think just to torment me, but fatherhood gave Frank more resolve and he over-ruled her as I told him he should. So the baby was baptised Aubrey Bevans.

I could see that Frank wanted to keep in my good graces and it soon became apparent why. Bishop Westfaling had discovered that Frank was the only Justice of the Peace in Herefordshire worth less than £20 in lands and he barely qualified to be a Member of Parliament when he was elected to represent Bishop's Castle.

Joan expressed concern to me about our son-in-law's casual attitude to practical matters, but he and everyone else was devoted to little Aubrey and Joan could hardly bear to part from Kate and the child, when we considered it safe to go back to London.

The time was drawing nigh when I would achieve my long held ambition: to acquire land for Samuel and his descendants.

7. Matters of Property

Fortune continued to smile on me, as it had on my fellow Salters. We now ranked ninth in order of the twelve Great Livery Companies. We took our part with them in the parades on religious holidays when the whole Company of the Fellowship, the Masters, Wardens, Assistants, Livery, Clerks, Beadles and Yeomen would dress in full regalia, each denoting his rank in the guild.

During the pageantry of the annual Lord Mayor's Parade, we proclaimed our new status and prosperity. In the procession of vessels, all painted and decorated with the colours of their guilds, the Salters' barge sailed up the Thames to Westminster Hall its blue and yellow flags flying in the wind. We led the Ironmongers, but followed behind the Haberdashers Company who took precedence. For Samuel, the day was filled with excitement and for Joan, the occasion always warranted a new gown.

Samuel had grown into a quiet and reserved boy, unlike his sister who had always been alert and energetic and never afraid to speak her mind - a dangerous trait as there was evidence daily to remind us. He was twelve by now and to my great disappointment, showed no disposition or ability to follow in my footsteps. So I determined that he should at least get an education sufficient for him to oversee the properties I intended to buy. After that, I would find him a suitable wife from a wealthy and established family, well connected and politically discreet – unlike a kinsman of ours, whose fate made it clear that discretion is always the better part of valour.

John Penry[1], for that was his name, openly criticised the Church's failings and as a result, was soon charged with harbouring Puritan leanings. Like many Londoners and some of my friends and fellow Salters, I tended to agree with his views, but we knew that heretical thoughts should remain as such, and that a wagging tongue often talked its way to the executioner's axe.

Lacking both restraint and discretion, John Penry set to and wrote and disseminated dangerous tracts with the inevitable consequences that in 1593 he was sent to trial. Cousin William, now Judge of Audience in the Court of Canterbury was among those who condemned him to death for his seditious writings.

William had no qualms about a kinsman paying such a price for his convictions. By now, my cousin had succeeded in becoming the most influential administrator in the Church of England and he was beyond such petty considerations. His power naturally aroused resentment and jealousy among his peers, especially the Bishop of St David's, who looked on William as an enemy and called him an 'insatiable cormorant'. To my relief, the man posed no threat - Cousin William's position remained secure.

We took young Samuel to Oxford and entered him into St John's College where his brother-in-law Frank had been a student twenty-five years earlier. I knew that manners and decorum had sadly deteriorated since then, but I made Samuel swear that he would not fall in with bad company, but learn restraint, and fear God's wrath - and mine - if he did.

Joan bade our son a tearful farewell as women are wont to do and I repeated the words I had often spoken to him, reminding him again of his obligations to me as my son, in spite of his failings. He said nothing but simply offered us a formal farewell. Then Joan and I continued on to the fresh cool air of Hereford again, she to see Kate and admire little Aubrey, and I to see what property could be bought or leased.

I was busy with legal matters too at this time. I had become involved in an unfortunate dispute involving Osterlow Grange, half way between Carmarthen and Haverford West, once part of the monastery of Whitland.

Osterlow Grange was supposedly owned by Sir John Perrott[2], who claimed to be the natural son of old King Henry. Those who knew him said he was very like His late Majesty in build and temperament, except that he had one fatal flaw: he never knew who his enemies were.

Sir John's foes soon revealed themselves when they discovered that he had once pronounced his views of Her Majesty to an assembled throng. They succeeded in proving that Sir John had said in a boastful and arrogant manner,

'Lo, now she is ready to piss herself for fear of the Spaniard. I am again one of her white haired boys!'

Evidence from the witnesses who had heard these words uttered, was enough to bring him down. As a result, he found himself in the Tower, charged with contemptuous words against the Queen and sentenced to death. As a consequence, because of his attainder for high treason, the Crown demanded Osterlow Grange back and so began a legal tug of war over the ownership of the property.

It became a complicated and nasty business, largely because of John Morgan Wolfe, a portly, pugnacious man who had taken it into his head to get possession of the property. He had a reputation for high-handedness, encouraging his men to enter and possess lands, especially when the occupant had just died. I didn't much like him, and suspected that he was only using me for his own ends, but then he was an astute businessman so I understood his motives.

In 1594, the Crown granted a new lease of Osterlow Grange to an old friend from my days in the cloth trade, Thomas Knyvet, a Gentleman of the Privy Chamber to the Queen. He decided he no longer wanted it, and conveyed the lease to me. I could see Osterlow Grange would be a shrewd investment. It promised a good return, with its messuages, mills and lands. As well, thirty stones of cheese, twenty-two rams, twenty-two lambs and twenty-two bushels of oats were payable each year by its tenants and farmers.

Years later, young Thomas did well when King James knighted him and gave him the Manor of Stanwell, in Middlesex. He gained even more favour when he involved himself in the hunt for the perpetrators of the plot to blow up the King and the Houses of Parliament on the evening of the fourth day of November 1605. He claimed it was to him that Guy Fawkes confessed, after he had been tortured for several days, of course.

Then the planets moved into their right spheres for me, for Sir Michael Blunt, an old acquaintance, unexpectedly offered me two properties in Herefordshire. Joan cared nothing for Osterlow Grange; it was far from Katherine and the baby in Hereford and a very long way from London, so I conveyed the lease to William Rogers of Laughame. He in turn conveyed it to John Morgan Wolfe.

The latter had what he had always wanted, and so did I, because one of Blunt's two properties I confidently expected would become the seat of the Aubrey family in coming generations. In time, it would serve for Samuel and his son's sons. That property was Clehonger Manor just four miles from the city of Hereford.

Clehonger and the other property Dorstone, both had proud histories. The estates had been in the hands of the Pembrugges and their descendants, the Barres and the Lysters since the thirteenth century. Clehonger Manor in particular made a great impression on Joan, standing as it did in such an open space with its surrounding farm and nearby fish pond - a far cry from our small Sign of the Black Swan in noisy Candlewick Street.

The large two-storey house stood back from the road and had enough rooms to accommodate a growing family and a well-laid out garden bursting with peonies, gilliflowers and lilies. You could see cattle grazing on the good fertile pasture, on land that rose gently from the banks of the River Wye a mile away, dotted with apple orchards between the small holdings of the yeomen farmers and labourers' hovels.

Not far from the manor stood the old parish church. A century ago the chantry on the east side of the churchyard became the Chapel of St Anne, licensed for one priest to pray for the souls of all Christians for ever.

Joan decided that Clehonger Manor would be a most suitable place for Samuel to live when the day came. It took us very little time to travel the road that led to the bridge over the River Wye and enter Hereford's city gates.

I made a good choice with Dorstone too. Although bigger than Clehonger and without some of its charm, it stood only twelve miles west of Hereford at the entrance to the beautiful Golden Valley of the River Dore where cornfields, orchards and rich grass meadows lay between the Black Mountains to the west and the gentler hills to the east. A few miles away, the old Cistercian abbey at Abbey Dore with its fourteenth century stained glass widows rose against the skyline.

It remained now for Samuel to prepare himself for the responsibilities of overseeing these estates that I had worked so hard to acquire.

Cousin William too, had prepared for the future of his children. He had bought the manors in Stretford and Burleton in Herefordshire not far from Clehonger, a farm in Sydenham in Kent and other estates in Breknockshire and Gloucestershire. These were in addition to Abercynrig, the house in which I grew up and which by rights should have come to me. My impecunious half-brother Richard had been forced to sell it. I rewarded myself with a smile of self-satisfaction and a glass or two of sack, at that news.

Cousin William's study in the great house he built at Brecknock looked onto the River Usk and he could ride nine miles together in his own land in the county. Although failing in health, he advised Sir Francis Walsingham on a range of legal matters and was still a favourite at Court. The Queen had granted 'her little doctor' lands in Brecknockshire and in Gloucestershire but by now, I had ceased to be envious of him.

Not even the fact that he had accumulated a huge fortune, or that he had the distinction of being the first private citizen in London to own a horse-drawn carriage, kindled any green in my eyes. I cannot say the same for Joan: such a means of transportation became the subject of lively conversation for many an hour in the Sign of the Black Swan.

Nevertheless, William had been a true kinsman and in the course of my selling Osterlow and buying Clehonger and Dorstone, he had tied me over with a bond for £40.

1. John Penry (1559-1603) Welsh Puritan with a passion for evangelising; criticised the Church authorities, which resulted in his execution for seditious writings.

2. Sir John Perrott (?1527-1592) Reputed bastard son of Henry VIII; a feud with the Archbishop of Dublin led to his disgrace and a dubious conviction of treason; died in the Tower of London.

8. Bonds & Broken Links

When we heard the news of the death of Cousin William in the winter of 1595, I went immediately to St Mary Abchurch and asked God to forgive me for all the unkind thoughts that I had ever harboured about him. Joan and I attended his grand funeral procession and did what we could to comfort his sons and daughters and poor distraught Wilgiford who had been married to him for forty years.

St Paul's Cathedral was overflowing with mourners, kinsmen and friends, ecclesiastics and fellow lawyers, and many elderly courtiers, their grey beards stark against their black gowns. I had to blink back the tears when Dr Daniel Dunne, his son-in-law, told the assembled congregation in a faltering voice,

'My dear father was a man of so courteous of disposition and affable of speech, so sweet of conversation and amiable in behaviour that there was never anyone in his position better beloved all his life'.

Sobs from his womenfolk filled the pause that followed his words. Among the mourners sat his clerk, Hugh George, weeping copiously. I never liked the man, he was ever ingratiating himself to me. I believed him to be false and untrustworthy, as indeed he proved to be. He lived in a house that his master had generously assigned to him, and William, blind to the man's faults, always referred to him as 'my loving and trusty servant'.

As sole executor of his will, Hugh George wrongly claimed that he had repaid the £110 that Cousin William had once borrowed from me. The next thing I heard, the man had taken off to Ireland with the best part of his late master's considerable fortune[1]. Wilgiford and her family bore this additional loss with great fortitude, but were powerless to retrieve the stolen money, notwithstanding the enraged protestations of his sons, Edward, Thomas and John.

William's children erected a monument to their father in bas-relief in St Paul's Cathedral depicting him surrounded by the kneeling figures of his three sons and six daughters.

It read thus:

Sacred to the Memory
Of Doctor William Aubrey
Descended from a conspicuous Family in Brecknock
He commenc't Doctor of the civil Laws in Oxford
Where he was also Regius Professor.
He was Auditor and Judge of Causes
Depending in the Arch-Bishop of Canterburies Courts,
And his Vicar-general in Spirituals.
Was Judge-Advocate of the Royal Army sent to St Quintins;
And one of the gret Council
Establisht in the Marches of Wales.
He was one of the Masters of Chancery,
And also one of the Masters of Requests,
To the Majesty of Queen Elizabeth.
In a word
Was a Person exquisitely well-learned
Of Singular Prudence, and of a most sweet, and winning disposition
Who
(Having by his Wife Wilgiford 3 Sons, and 6 Daughters)
On the 23rd of July 1595 in the 66th year of his age
Resigned his Soul to his Redeemer
And here awaiteth for his second coming.
Sir Edward, and Sir Thomas Aubrey Knights
Together with their Brother John Aubrey Esquire,
Their 3 surviving sons have with much sadness Consecrated this Marble to
his Memory.

As for my own son and heir, on his visits home from Oxford, all he could talk about were stories of the sea, and for this I must hold myself in part responsible. I told him how we Salters had made a considerable contribution to Her Majesty's Navy and he heard Joan and me discussing at length how much many marks we would put into the next Salters' joint stock-venture. The Guild's aim in this regard was to fit out twelve ships and two pinnaces in preparation for an attack against Spain and we confidently expected to reap a handsome reward from part of the prize money.

Samuel announced to his mother one day that he wanted to run away and join Sir Walter Raleigh and Robert Harcourt in their expedition to Guiana to beat the Spanish and find El Dorado. The fear of my wrath and the thought of her distress dissuaded him from such a foolish idea. He sulked for days afterwards.

Joan and I had more serious matters to contend with. Three successive years of bad harvests brought high food prices for those who could afford to eat, and death from starvation for those who could not. Another visitation of the plague made us wonder what terrible sins had been committed, to warrant such misery.

Joan and I did what we could to help those of our fellow Salters who had been afflicted. We gave a sum of money to the new almshouse in Monkwell Street that we Salters had founded with the bequest left by Sir Ambrose Nicholas and gave what we could to the poor of the parish. Even so, people died in the streets from cold and hunger.

We were still at war with Spain, declared or not, in that year of 1596 and at last we heard the news of the Earl of Essex's fleet and its great victory. The Queen's favourite, the Lord High Admiral and Sir Walter Raleigh had led an expedition to Spain, enticing hundreds of gentlemen adventurers from all over the country, eager for excitement, for fighting and still more for plunder, to join them.

On the ships' arrival in Spanish waters, and after a few hours' fierce battle in which the enemy fleet was utterly defeated, Essex put to land with 3,000 men and drove all before him until he entered the market place at Cadiz[2] The town surrendered and soon his flag was fluttering from the citadel. Before the fleet sailed home in triumph, Essex created a total of sixty-four knights, much we heard, to the chagrin of our good Queen.

On their return, as the fleet sailed up the Thames in triumph, church bells rang across London and the whole City was came alive with excitement. Joan put on her silk gown embroidered with sprigs of field flowers, yellow and blue – the Salters' colours - that she loved so much, and we both went to the Salters' Hall to celebrate the occasion.

Cheering crowds packed into St Paul's churchyard for the Thanksgiving Service in the Cathedral where Essex was eulogised from the pulpit amid applause from the congregation. We thanked God for our good fortune, remembering how we had all rejoiced and celebrated the defeat of the Spanish Armada eight years before, as well.

Young Samuel could talk of nothing else. He continued to complain that he should have gone with them and then the Earl of Essex would have knighted him, as he did Gelly Meyrick and Richard Rudhall and James Scudamore, all men from Herefordshire, as was the hero of the hour. I sharply reminded him that he should get on with his studies, if he had such a desire to please Her Majesty.

Early one morning we were awakened early to the sounds of cries and a strange commotion coming from the direction of Bread Street. To our dismay we saw smoke billowing skywards and our worst fears were realised. Our Salters' Hall was burning fiercely and it was soon apparent that little could be done to save it.

We put the cause of the disaster down to the gunpowder stored in the armoury. The building always held an arsenal of muskets and helmets, pikes and breastplates, to fit out members for any general muster of the citizens of London. The loss meant an outlay of money to build another Salters' Hall – the third - on that site. Prosperous or not, none of us relished the thought of such a contribution, but we owed it to our great guild.

My words to Samuel must have fallen on receptive ears, because he graduated from St John's College to everyone's satisfaction. I then paid £4 for his entrance fee to the Middle Temple and had him bound with Henry Williams and John Vaughan, two of my associates from Herefordshire. I expected Samuel to complete his studies and grasp enough law to be competent in running the estates that he would eventually inherit.

Apart from my owning estates in Herefordshire, nothing seemed to interest him, much less further study. Joan feared he would succumb to temptation and fall in with undesirable company. Disorderly and riotous behavior had increased markedly in London, especially on Shrove Tuesday when the apprentices took their traditional holiday.

Drunken mobs of notorious roaring boys from the Inns of Court annoyed decent citizens and spent their time carousing in taverns and brawling. Samuel admitted to liking a pint or two of ale, especially at the nearby Mermaid Inn in Bread Street where he enjoyed meeting the wits of the day, but he promised his mother he would do nothing to bring shame on the Aubrey name.

Church bells rang in the new year and the new century. Someone placed an urn of well water on the altar of St Mary Abchurch to bless its magical qualities and even though people objected because it smacked of Catholic superstition, it remained in place.

People exchanged gifts to celebrate the new year and compared astrological almanacs. I remember one of the most popular was *Erra Pater,* that had a table forecasting the weather according to the day of the week on which the new year began.

I needed no almanac to tell me that Kate's husband, Frank Bevans would soon cost me money.

It became increasingly apparent that he had no head for financial matters and I had to agree with Joan - reluctantly - that Kate might suffer for it. The man owned Bridgecourt Farm at Kingstone, not far from Clehonger. It had been the subject of several court cases over the years and he owed about a thousand marks. I gave in to Joan's persuasion and bought the property from him. My gesture was not entirely altruistic, for it yielded an annual rent of £10 and had once been owned by John Scudamore, a member of one of Herefordshire's oldest families. It would do us no harm to have such a connection, however remote.

The Scudamores were connected with the Rudhalls and I had entered into negotiations with William Rudhall of Rudhall to marry Samuel to his daughter Joyce. Her sister Frances was married to Herbert Westfaling, grandson of the Bishop of Hereford and my Kate had taken it upon herself to promote the match. I had to admit it looked to be a most suitable union, the Rudhalls being such a well-established family linked to many other important ones throughout the county.

Old William Rudhall was a bluff countryman with a ruddy face, only interested in his extensive property, his many horses and lamenting the antagonism between two of his sons, John and William. I felt a surge of envy when I thought how lucky he was to have sired four sons and only one of them die. The eldest, Sir Richard Rudhall had been knighted at Cadiz and Samuel was already excited at the prospect of being his brother.

Joyce was the fourth of William Rudhall's seven daughters, a quiet, unassuming young woman, who appeared to believe that Samuel would make her a good husband. Joan lovingly admonished me, when I expressed my doubts to her about this, and of course she was right as she usually was. We did agree that Samuel still showed little aptitude for handling money, and it concerned me that his father-in-law, for all his extended land holdings had borrowed heavily from local scriveners, and his ward.

Sir Walter Pye, the husband of Johanna, another of William Rudhall's daughters, was said to be one of the wealthiest men in England. He was Attorney-General of the Court of Wards and Liveries and had appointed William Rudhall guardian to a wealthy young orphan whose money was too readily available.

My mind slipped back - as it did so easily these days - to the time after little Marjorie's death when I went to the Guildhall to sign a recognisance and put up £93 for a newly orphaned child. That one had been the first of four such orphans for whom I had stood surety, taking my involvement over the years, as I remember, to £643. Times had changed since then; Citizens of London, looked after their own.

So two years into another century, Joan and I welcomed Joyce Rudhall as a new daughter and Samuel looked more cheerful than I'd seen him for many a moon. The marriage took place at Brampton Abbotts, the Rudhall's parish church just north of Ross-on-Wye. All of Joyce's many sisters and brothers and their children and even William Rudhall's tenants brought them presents and flowers to see them on their way to a happy future.

Only one black spot marred the joyous occasion that year, and that was my appearance in the Court of Chancery. When I bought Bridgecourt from Frank, I had no inkling that it would be the subject of litigation and that I would be forced to defend myself over the subject of a lease – of which I knew nothing. Frank had told me only that Bridgecourt had previously been owned by John Scudamore, who died soon after Frank bought it. The claimants in the case alleged that it had long been leased to one Edward Spencer now also dead, and it was to his estate that the annual rent was now due.

Frank, looking ill and with shaking hands, told the Court to which we were bidden, that shortly after Scudamore's death, he went to his house to ascertain if the previous owner had left any papers concerning Bridgecourt. His widow gave him permission to make a search. Frank looked through the late John Scudamore's papers but found nothing.

He told the Court that he chanced to look in a settle but it contained only waste papers and writing, thrust together. Then he noticed some parchments, four of which concerned Bridgecourt. They were indeed all leases, but cancelled.

He swore to the Court that he had taken the papers home with him and given them to my niece Elizabeth Taylor, my sister's daughter who was staying with me at the time, with instructions that she send them to me. At this point, my memory failed me and Samuel, who was by my side during these proceedings, bade me be seated.

The whole case cast aspersions on our family: Frank, who may or may not have given the papers to Elizabeth as he claimed; my niece who may have failed to carry out the instructions that Frank gave her, or not; and me, because the leases could have disproved my right to the land. Without them, Bridgecourt still belonged to me.

Nevertheless I sold the property as soon as I conveniently could and almost immediately afterwards, Frank fell ill with a dangerous sickness and died. As was expected, he left his affairs in a parlous state. Having failed to appoint an executor for his will, Kate was left to administer his estate, deal with his bonds and mortgages, and pay his creditors.

Frank asked to be buried in Hereford Cathedral and bequeathed a gilt cup to its Bishop and a piece of plate to Joan and me, to be chosen at the discretion of his wife. Samuel was happy to acquire his best gray gelding. His property, after bequests, went to Kate until young Aubrey reached the age of twenty-one. I had to admit that she untangled the web of her husband's finances with an energy and astuteness not often found in a woman, qualities that I searched for in vain in her brother.

But then in a matter of only weeks, Kate immediately succumbed to the alleged charms of a rake and ne'er do well, Sir William Herbert, and insisted on marrying the man. I warned her, that if she disobeyed me, widow or no widow, I would cut her out of my will. She did, and I did, in spite of Joan's pleas.

Kate was patently infatuated, and blind to the many defects that I and most others saw in him. Even though his uncle had been Cousin William's patron and we were distantly related, a point in his favour, he was over thirty years older than she, and had sired only illegitimate children. This latter mollified me to some extent, as any children Kate might give the man, would inherit before his bastards.

His litany of faults began when he sold the estates of his first wife, the co-heiress of the great Penrhyn estate in Carnarvonshire to finance the leases of coal mines in the Gower. He had actions brought against him in the Court of Star Chamber; he had illegally disposed of Crown property and he had been fined a thousand marks for intimidating the citizens of Cardiff. He had used a posse of four hundred ne'er-do-wells to overawe the town, leaving the bailiffs helpless, the town in an uproar and peaceful citizens of Cardiff afraid to stir abroad.

I suspected that part of the man's attraction was his taste for opulent living and his sumptuous house on the site of the Grey Friars in Cardiff that was supposed to be a wonder for all men to see. Only Joan, indulgent to her as ever, attended her marriage at St Mary Abchurch on the sixth day of July in the year of Our Lord, 1602. I despaired of Kate and despised the extravagance and foolishness of her new husband.

1. William Aubrey's descendants (including the John Aubrey of *Brief Lives*) were still trying to retrieve his fortune, without success, well into the seventeenth century.

2. The poet John Donne (1571-1631) witnessed the dreadful scene at Cadiz and summed it up in an epigram: 'They in the sea being burnt, they in the burnt ship drowned.' At the moment of victory, Essex threw his hat into the sea for joy, and Raleigh ordered a fanfare of trumpets.

9. Death & Life

One day, I decided it was time to pay a visit to my old friend and kinsman Dr John Dee at Mortlake. In my heart I knew it would be the last. We had been born in the same year, but under such different astral influences!

A man of infinite capacity, he had thrived in a universe vaster than mine, one in which he helped encompass the ideas of Gerard Mercator who drew lines on parchment so that men could see with their own eyes what lay beyond the horizon. He speculated on what they called the North West Passage and the mysterious Terra Australis and his guidance had influenced many a joint-stock company, some of which I had been pleased to be a part.

He greeted me cheerfully enough, but I saw at once that matters had deteriorated. The scene confirmed the stories I had heard that he had been forced to sell some of his precious books to pay for food. He had never really recovered from the terrible time when mobs ransacked his house and library, believing him to be an evil magician.

It was unthinkable that I should offer him money in his distress - instead we talked of old times. He stroked his milk-white beard and regaled me with tales of his many travels into Europe and the welcome he received from Emperor Rudolf the Second at Prague. In the course of our conversation, a question sprang to my lips that manners and decorum had, before, dissuaded me from uttering.

It concerned a particular event, an exchange of wives, a story that had never died but had echoed tirelessly down the years. I broached it tentatively.

'The Covenant with God you once told me that you and your wife Jane, together with Edward Kelly and his young wife Joan, made – was that anything *more* than a spiritual exchange? Was it also an exchange of er, – certain favours of a somewhat delicate and intimate kind – among the four of you, as some have claimed?'

John only glanced at me and then stared into his distant memories.

'Spring in Bohemia – their hair like the gold we'd transmuted – and the angels who appeared - we consummated our friendship – *pactu – factu*.' So the agreement had been done, performed. I had needs be content with his cryptic answer and manners dictated I pursue the matter no further.

Providence had favoured us both with a long life but there were almost too many tumultuous moments for us to remember or dwell on. John held that the key to a happy old age was to anticipate a positive future and reminded me that with death, came birth. Both were merely two sides of one equation - that of life itself.

***

The Queen was coming to the end of her life, as was I, and the times were still uncertain. There were men abroad for whom ambition overrode all consideration of prudence and wisdom. They were swayed by sweet words and heeded not the consequences of their deeds.

Sir Gelly Meyrick, an associate of Cousin William, was one such. Knighted by the Earl of Essex at Cadiz, and now faced with financial ruin in his desire to acquire more and more land, he joined his former leader and played a key part in his treasonous plot against the Queen.

Essex paraded down Fleet Street with his followers. Then, on the eve of the planned uprising, we learned that he paid 40 shillings to Augustine Phillips of Shakespeare's acting company, the Lord Chamberlain's Men, for a performance of Richard II with the notorious abdication scene included.

When the foolish cause inevitably withered before it had even borne fruit, the traitors were promptly arrested, convicted of treason and sentenced to death. The Earl of Essex, still revered by his followers, was executed and Sir Gelly Meyrick was hanged at Tyburn, in full view of the jeering crowds. So much the great had fallen.

I missed hearing the snippets of Court news now Cousin William was dead, but Joan assured me that Her Majesty still wore the ring that Essex had given her and that she regularly rode ten miles on horseback in a single day and that she still hunted. But the next winter took its toll and with it, between the hours of two and three in the morning of the twenty-fourth day of March in the Year of our Lord 1603, our beloved Gloriana left this life as the most resplendent Sun setting at last in a western cloud.

The Queen was dead and we begged God to save the King.

I suffered only a few of the symptoms of old age in spite of Joan's unwarranted concerns, when, each year, I added yet another to the sum of my life's seasons.

On the death of the Queen, a new King descended into our midst, bringing with him another visitation of the plague, harvesting deaths too many to count. Yet nothing could dampen the enthusiasm that greeted the Scottish Monarch. Amid great pomp and ceremony in the Royal Gardens at Whytehall, King James knighted many courtiers, among them, Joyce's uncle and royal pensioner, James Croft.

Joyce remained at Clehonger, too occupied to attend the grand occasion. I had made over my two properties in Herefordshire to Samuel and they had now fitted out Clehonger Manor House to her taste and satisfaction. She was giving birth to their son and heir, on whom they bestowed the name Herbert, after her brother-in-law Herbert Westfaling who had agreed to be the child's godfather. I wished to have his horoscope drawn, but I could not impinge on my friendship with John Dee again.

The next year, Samuel and Joyce pleased us with a visit to London. She was with child again but she brought her maid and a wet nurse, for whom Joan arranged suitable beds in our Sign of the Black Swan. I was gratified to see that Samuel had grown stouter, and was full of stories of Herefordshire society in general and his fellow brothers-in-law in particular. It worried me though that he seemed fearful of my questions concerning his tenants and whether they all paid their rents in full and on time or not.

One night during their stay, Joan and I heard a commotion. Joyce was in labour - before her time. It was a tiny girl baby and Samuel insisted she be baptised at once in case she died without God's blessing and spend eternity in hell. Joan knew what I thought of such nonsense, but a look from her made me hold my tongue.

The next day, they took the little bundle to St Mary Abchurch and christened her Katherine, which reminded me of my ungrateful daughter. Sensing my discomfort, Joyce promised me she would call the next boy Morgan and the next girl Joan. And this she did.

At Joan's insistence, I wrote my will and made her, my well beloved wife, my executrix. Samuel could look forward to inheriting the lease of Shelwyck, some two miles from the city of Hereford, a property I had recently bought of Thomas Wigmore, as well as owning the Sign of the Black Swan after Joan's death. I saw that my few remaining relatives and my servants were adequately cared for, and left money to the poor people in Christ's Hospital, the orphanage and school, to St Thomas' Hospital in Southwark and the poor in our parish of St Mary Abchurch.

Both Joan and I bequeathed money to our wonderful fraternity of Salters for a dinner to be held on the day of our funerals. But Joan, compassionate and practical as ever, declared she would do more than give money for a dinner that would soon be forgotten after being eaten. In her will, she would leave £100 to the Company, which sum would be put out every year at 5% interest, $4\frac{1}{2}$% to be distributed to the poor widows of Salters and the remaining $\frac{1}{2}$% for the use of the Company for ever.

As is often the case in one's second childhood, thoughts drift back to one's first, and memories of the poverty-stricken families in Llanfrynach suffering and struggling to survive, that as a boy I thought nothing of, now came back to haunt me. I decided that they too, should receive an annuity. So I bought a farm near Dorstone in Herefordshire and determined that a rent of £4 from that property should be annually distributed among the poor of parish where I lived as a child.

Samuel shifted uneasily in his seat, when we advised him of this future Christian obligation he would be obliged to fulfil. Even reminding him of my hard-won prosperity that he would soon inherit without a modicum of effort on his part, did not engender any degree of enthusiasm in him. Joan urged him to answer before God that he would perform this obligation to me, and this he grudgingly did.

A great occasion, too important to miss, was the celebration in 1607 in the newly built Salters' Hall when His Majesty came in person and awarded us a new Charter to replace the one the old Queen had given us. Joan wore a new gown for the ceremony, one with a high lace collar and matching lace cuffs and even though her hair was quite grey, looked just as lovely as she did when we first met, too many years ago now, to remember. In my best livery and walking with the aid of a stick, I followed the Master and two Wardens into the crowded hall, festooned with garlands of yellow flowers and filled with so many of my friends.

The Master of the Mystery and the new Wardens were crowned with the usual pomp and ceremony, then names were called for the positions of Assistant. Mine was among them and the entire Company voted for me. Amid the cheers, a loving cup of ale was passed around clockwise with the man passing it, standing to protect the drinker's back. We Salters never forgot this ancient ceremony of symbolising mutual protection. I thereafter headed the list of twenty-four in the new Court of Assistants in the King's Charter as 'Our Beloved Morgan Aubrey'. Joan wept with pride and joy.

A year later, my old friends Richard Staper and Nicholas Blinco nominated me and I was sworn in as an Alderman of Aldgate Ward. The next day, I felt unwell and Joan insisted I ask to be discharged on the plea of old age, which I duly was. The fine of £300 I had to pay more than compensated for all the entertaining and other expenditure expected of me in such a position. As always, Joan was right.

After that time, I seldom ventured out, content only to receive callers, particularly my old friends George Samwell and Thomas Vickers. They went regularly to the Royal Exchange and on their visits to the Sign of the Black Swan would relay the latest developments in the 'positive future' of this new century. By now, the Virginia Company of London had been granted a Royal Charter and across the seas in the New World, Jamestown had been founded.

Closer to home, and of more interest to me, the government was farming all customs revenue to a consortium of London merchants for an annual rent. I knew some of the names being considered and Joan had to dissuade me with stern words and veiled threats from sallying forth to become one of them. She now rarely left my side.

The summer before, she and I had visited her nephew Robert Vaux at the Manor of Whipsnade in Bedfordshire, some forty miles away. The coach ride was more onerous now, but I had to admit a grudging admiration when we inspected his choice, for which he had paid £1,500. The house boasted sixteen rooms and stood on two hundred and sixty-eight acres of land. The property's total annual value came to £100 and the timber on the estate was worth £300. The young man knew good value when he saw it, and once again, my thoughts turned to Samuel and wished that he too could have been blessed with such an aptitude. I could only pray that little Herbert grow strong and inherit those estates that I had left to his father.

Kate, now Lady Herbert, was leading an exciting life in Cardiff and hardly missed her sedate existence in Hereford, in spite of the stormy marriage with her second husband. Her son Aubrey Bevans, now a strapping fifteen-year-old and the apple of Joan's eye, had entered St John's College, Oxford. He had survived an unsympathetic step-father and had plans to study at Lincoln's Inn after his graduation.

Samuel was content to lead the life of a country gentleman. He was now the father of three children, all thriving and most likely more to come. I thought back to his horoscope as I so often did now: a fortunate life and fruitful marriage, but a future peril would subject him to some trial or tribulation. I wished him many more sons from the fruit of his loins and could only pray that his careful upbringing and the integrity of his character would shield him against any harm, and that he would face any adversity with fortitude.

Looking back over my life, a few regrets returned to bring me unease. I had always taken my Uncle John's advice to fight for every penny that was rightly mine, but on rare occasions the fight ended badly and left a sour taste in my throat. Owen ap Jevan Bedowe, a fellow countryman I had helped when he arrived in London, owed me money for a long time - I remember the exact sum, £12-16s - and I was forced to take him to the Court of Pleas. I was awarded 21 shillings but the man could not or would not repay me and he ended up in prison.

It was a sad business. Joan spoke her mind as she always did, and asked how could a man pay his debts if he was locked away in the Fleet? I could find no sensible answer.

Such cases aside, on reflection, I could not but indulge in a degree of self-satisfaction in all I had achieved, and I now slept well o'nights. I had done my best for Samuel, whose own son Herbert would in turn beget sons well into the 'positive future'.

In the darkness of a freezing winter's evening in January 1608, with Joan's warm body beside mine, I felt her tears flow onto my face and seep into my beard. I remembered nothing more. That moment became an eternity.

Herbert Aubrey II

Royalist of Herefordshire

Herbert Aubrey (1603-1671) = Elizabeth Bedell (1609-1676)
|

  1. Anne

      2. Samuel Aubrey (Herbert Aubrey's son & heir)

         3. *Herbert Aubrey II , M.P.* (1631-1691) = Joyce Brydges

            4. Mary 5. Elizabeth 6. Mathew

               7. Judith

                 8. Godwin

                   9. Thomas

|

   1. Herbert Aubrey III (1664-1744) = 1) Judith Cole
                              = 2) Rebecca Gwillym
                              = 3) Debora Hopton

10. The Aubreys of Clehonger

The scenes play themselves time and again in my mind, as I lie here on this bed of pain: the terrible journey in the dogger from Ireland, that Godforsaken place, with Joyce vomiting from the surging swell and Betty doing her best to comfort her moaning mother and she blaming me, her Lord and Master, for all the ills that have beset us; I, summoning every fibre of my being, praying to God for endurance and our safe return to England; and then seeing with relief in the distance at last, appearing and disappearing in the swell, the flickering lights of Chester.

I thought being on dry land, thanks be to God, and recovering my strength in the inn, the best that I could afford, that our perils were behind us, but no. I had directed Betty to go and supervise the last of our trunks, when a few minutes later she burst back into our chamber without so much as a knock, a 'Papa, by your leave' or even a curtsey.

'The Earl of Shrewsbury has ordered your arrest!', she stammered, 'I overheard the Mayor talking to the Innkeeper. We must leave Chester at once! You are suspected of ill designs!'

Then I saw Betty's pale face, my wife moaning and wringing her hands, with my own head in a whirl, wondering which of my enemies had instigated this folly.

Ill designs! Those two words belie everything onto which I and my family have anchored our lives. In the time of the Troubles, was not my Uncle Morgan murdered by a horde of Irish barbarians? Was not my grandfather taken prisoner by the Puritans and transported to Bristol? Was not our manor house partly destroyed when the Scots army besieged Hereford? And did not my dear father suffer the indignities of being fined for 'being on his estate when it was held a garrison against Parliament'? Ill designs, indeed!

Of course there was the money I owed His Majesty. It took me years to repay it, after many sacrifices but thanks be to God, I have always had friends in high places: Lord Danby who saved me from bankruptcy; Sir Joseph Williamson my Fellow Archer from Oxford days; Sir Leoline Jenkins; and of course my Lord Rochester.

Before he unhappily fell out of favour with His Majesty, His Lordship himself recommended me to His Majesty as a Commissioner of Revenue in Ireland. He even paid me the courtesy of calling me 'honest' to my face. In their day, when James the Second graced the throne, those men had the ear of His Majesty – not now, not when his daughter and son-in-law, Mary and William of Orange wear the Royal Crowns as Queen and King of England.

As for my son – Oh Absalom, my son Absalom! How hast thou forsaken me! To be beguiled by the daughter of Puritans! To be accused by my son of simple-mindedness and credulity when all I sought was to do my utmost to uphold the Divine Right of Kings! He gave me endless burdens to bear.

In spite of all that has happened, I take comfort in the fact that my first loyalties, as I doubt his to be, have always been to Almighty God, to my Church (the Anglican Church of course and the Book of Common Prayer) to my King (*the King ordained by succession and the Grace of God*) and my Country - and of course to my kith and kin. The Aubreys of Clehonger, unlike many families of our acquaintance, were then, and have always been, united as one in their loyalty and service and devotion to the Monarch.

Looking back on my life, I can aver that I have never brought shame upon myself by knowingly doing any wrong to my fellow man. I have always pursued my undertakings with commitment and dedication, aspects of my life and character that I suspect were often the source of envy among my peers. Would that many of my contemporaries had been so blessed with such fealties, when put to the test!

Of course my father bred me up to be a loyal subject of His Majesty. He urged me to be proud of the distinction of the family into which I was born and my Welsh heritage even though the intricacies of the language eluded me, the few times I sought to enlarge my meagre knowledge of it.

Even at the risk of being accused of the sin of Pride, I can state that we are descended from the Counts of Normandy who crossed the Channel with William the Conqueror. Sir Reginald Aubrey, brother of the Count of Boulogne and Danmartin, Earl Marshal of France, helped Bernard Neumarché in his conquest of Brecon and was rewarded with the manors of Slwch and Abercynrig. He married a daughter of Richard Clare, Earl of Brionne, one of the most important men in England. Thus the Aubreys settled into Wales and extended their influence on that country.

Closer to my immediate family can be counted Dr William Aubrey, whom that great Queen Elizabeth, God rest her soul, called her 'little Doctor'. My great-grandfather Morgan Aubrey was his cousin and a life-long friend. Growing up in Wales and being almost the same age, they played together as children – I believe in peace and harmony – a fact that surely cemented their friendship when they both left the land of their birth and made their mark on the world.

My grandfather told me that in the course of Dr Aubrey's life, even monarchs called upon his vast knowledge of the law. The Catholic Queen Mary sent him to France as Judge Advocate of her army there and he frequently gave legal advice to Sir Francis Walsingham, one of the most powerful men in Queen Elizabeth's court.

Yet his fame and learning attracted enemies. These vipers in his bosom spread false tales about him abroad – as we who live righteous lives know only too well to expect. Even on his deathbed, they said that he called for a Catholic priest to be given the last rites – an unbelievable story considering that he left this earthly life as the most influential administrator in the Church of England!

Both he and my great-grandfather Morgan Aubrey died rich, as did my great-grandmother, who left over one thousand pounds to her grandchildren and to the poor and needy.

Unhappily I did not inherit their knack of accumulating money. In fact, I died burdened with debts that pulled me early down to the grave, but they were ones that many a man in my position in life would have incurred, also given the calls on my Christian charity. Then there were the betrayals of trust that I was called upon to suffer. I put my faith in and gave my financial support to a number of friends and in particular to a kinsman, to my very great cost.

Such were the scourges that fate bestowed upon me. I have heard my enemies whisper that my woes were only of my own making, but who can tell which of one's many ills God has called upon one to suffer, as Christ did upon the cross?

This curse, that of lacking the root of all evil (although no one ever charged me with being guilty of the *love* of it, unlike most of my acquaintance), continued to envelope me throughout my life, no matter how much I implored Our Lord to lift it from my shoulders. My one consolation is that I bore this life-long burden with great fortitude.

I began my life in 1631, as the second son of a prosperous Herefordshire family of considerable standing in the community, thanks in the main to our great-grandfather's wealth. I was born the year after our beloved sovereign to be, King Charles the Second first honoured the world with his presence. In my secret heart, I saw him as a brother for whom I would lay down my life, if ever called upon to do so.

My father, Herbert Aubrey of Clehonger, was the eldest son of Sir Samuel Aubrey, graciously knighted by King James I, in the course of His Majesty's Western Progress in 1620. Some cynics have said that the honour only reflected the fact that at the time my grandfather enjoyed the status of a wealthy landowner, in a position to buy his title, not that he had ever shown physical loyalty to his King on the field of battle. In fact, those heroic deeds would come later.

Kate, my grandfather's only surviving sister who died before I was born, was not close to her brother either in years or in temperament. When he talked of Great-Aunt Kate, reputed to be a beautiful woman with brown laughing eyes, my grandfather's tone of voice would change markedly. 'Strong willed! Selfish and unfeeling!' he would shout. That was how he usually described her, the few times he mentioned her name – or that of her third husband – in our hearing.

Her father had chosen her first husband, Dr Francis Bevans, a Justice of the Peace and Chancellor of the diocese of Hereford. His Bishop at the time, Herbert Westfaling, was connected to us by his son, also Herbert, marrying my grandmother's sister, Frances

Morgan Aubrey = *Joan Vaux*	
(c1527-1608) *(d.1614)*	
|	
1. Kate Aubrey =	*1) Dr Francis Bevans*
(1572-1617)	*(d.1602)*
	2) Sir William Herbert
	(c1539-1609)
	3) Sir Anthony St John
	(d.1638)
2. Samuel Aubrey = *Joyce Rudhall*	
(1580-1645) *(c1585-1638)*	

Rudhall. That most suitable of matches ended when Dr Bevans died.

Aubrey Bevans, Great-Aunt Kate's son from that marriage, went to his father's old college at Oxford, St John's and then Lincoln's Inn as a student. I remember my grandfather being particularly incensed at the fact that in her will, his mother favoured Aubrey over all her other grandchildren. She left him £200, a feather bed with bolsters, blankets, furniture, a silver bowl and six silver spoons.

Although a distant kinsman and well connected, Great-Aunt Kate's second husband, Sir William Herbert behaved in a riotous and unpredictable manner. She married him against her father's wishes and those of my grandfather as well. My grandfather grudgingly admitted that Sir William had been Sheriff of Carmarthenshire, Mayor of Cardiff and a member of the Council in the Marches of Wales. He built a sumptuous house on the site of the Grey Friars in Cardiff that people said was a wonder for all to see. 'Doubtless, a considerable part of the man's appeal,' my grandfather snorted.

His death made Great-Aunt Kate a wealthy widow and for her third husband, she chose a man considerably younger than she, Sir Anthony St John, the third son of Oliver, the third Baron St John of Bletsoe. They sent the child she bore him, Oliver St John, to Sidney Sussex College Cambridge, a hotbed of Puritanism, where that regicide-to-be, Oliver Cromwell, became his fellow student.

My older sister Anne, for whom the story of our Great-Aunt held an unwarranted fascination, lamented the fact that we were too young to have known her. For me, beautiful as she may have

(Sir) Samuel Aubrey	=	Joyce Rudhall
(1580-1645)		(c1585-1638)
1. Herbert Aubrey	=	Elizabeth Bedell
(1603-1671)		(1609-1676)
2. Anthony Aubrey		
(d.1679)		
3. Joane	=	Thomas Emley of Helmdon,
(b.c1606)		Northants
4. Morgan Aubrey		
(1607-1641)		

been, she obviously lacked that essential requirement of feminine graces, a dutiful obedience to her father and brother – not to mention her affiliation with a family of dubious loyalty to the Church of England.

The Aubreys became well established in Clehonger, on the estate near the village of that name, south of the River Wye, not far from the city of Hereford. Our great-grandfather Morgan Aubrey purchased the property towards the end of the last century.

The old house remained much the same as when my grandfather and his bride first resided in it after their marriage in 1602. It was at Clehonger Manor that my father and his two brothers Anthony and

Morgan were born and their sister Joane. She married Thomas Emley and went to live in Helmdon, Northamptonshire. Unhappily, distance contributed to the looseness of Aunt Joane's ties with my family.

Clehonger Manor stood back from the road that lead to the village and was approached by a long drive. I believe my grandmother planned the existing garden with its herbaceous borders and rows of lilies, roses, buttercups and pinks, shaded by a line of elm trees.

Across the road, the old Norman church, All Saints, beckoned the whole village every Sunday to hear the parson's words. On days of special services in the Church calendar we children would accompany our parents, dressed in our best jackets and bonnets, following behind them to the front pew. My little brothers would be sternly admonished if they ever swung their legs, or made my sisters giggle. We all dutifully repeated the catechism and then my older brother and I were expected to answer my father's questions concerning the finer points of the sermon – a task more often than not I excelled at, and therefore enjoyed.

My earliest memory of the manor house is the hall with its impressive Spanish table and six straight-backed leather chairs lining the walls like sentinels, as if guarding the Aubrey arms, wrought in painted plaster, set high above one wall. Our parents would entertain their guests in the great parlour, to which we children would be bidden to present ourselves on special occasions.

One winter's day, when we were forced to remain indoors because of heavy rain, Anne and I discovered a tiny room, secreted behind some panelling. Its only light and air came from a wide cob-webbed crack high up in one wall and venturing inside, we could see a dark flight of narrow steps leading down to the floor below.

'It's a priest's hole!' Anne decided. 'Papa's study is down there! I think there's another door behind his chest of drawers!' We both shivered with excitement, Anne more than I, and we beat a hasty retreat for fear the room was haunted, perhaps by the ghost of a priest. We vowed to keep its existence secret, even from my older brother Samuel and the other children.

11. Rudhalls of Rudhall

All of our rooms and chambers, even the little parlour and the withdrawing room seemed to us when we were children, to be large and imposing – until we visited the stately old residence Rudhall Manor, situated on the border dividing the parishes of Ross and Brampton Abbots. It belonged to our grandmother's family. She was Joyce, the daughter of William Rudhall and this estate played a large part in my future expectations.

On the first occasion I can remember visiting Rudhall Manor, its drive, lined with sweet chestnuts, seemed endless and the house itself, set in a great parkland, struck me as immense. Built long ago, it boasted the emblem of the Prince of Wales, a plume of feathers within a garter, to reflect the fact that it had been erected by William Rudhall, Attorney-General to Edward, Prince of Wales and son of Henry VI. Its wonderful stone entrance, two storeys high, and the ceiling beams and pendants in the great hall made our residence pale into insignificance.

It even boasted its very own chapel, dedicated to St Catherine, where the family worshipped. But we loved the round stone tower best. It rose cold and dark, lit only by slits in the walls beside its spiral staircase that led to the turret several levels above. Our Great-Aunt Mary Rudhall told us that when her older brother John returned from his Grand Tour, he found part of the north wing had been damaged by fire so had the tower built to hide the missing section.

Anne swore that the ghost of a Norman knight had made it his home. He had been brutally killed by a local Saxon lord and vowed he would not rest until he had sought revenge. After many thorough searches – without Samuel who was too afrighted to come, even though we explored the tower in broad daylight - we could find no evidence of the apparition.

We decided that only a visitation in the darkness would decide the story once and for all, and that just as soon as we were old enough, we would spend a night there. Then we would force Samuel to come with us. I remember he howled in distress when we told him what lay in store for him and went running to our mother. She sent us to bed hungry that night as a punishment and we hated him all the more.

The next day, I convinced my brother that our manor house was haunted by the ghost of a priest who had died in a secret hole that we had discovered above our father's study. At first he refused to believe me, but then screamed as terror overtook him. I remember running away before any punishment could be inflicted on me.

Our grandmother Rudhall's father William, had sired four sons and seven daughters, whose off-spring provided endless topics of conversation among the adults. I knew that we children were not supposed to listen to their gossip and criticisms, but my sister Anne had a great curiosity and a prodigious memory. When appealed to for a sufficient length of time, she would reluctantly tell us all she knew of our cousins, often finding it difficult to hide her eagerness to reveal the latest tale she had gleaned.

Richard Rudhall the eldest son, handsome beyond compare, according to Anne, who had heard our grandmother extol his virtues, had been one of the many young men knighted by Essex after his successful naval expedition to Cadiz. A year later, Sir Richard caught a fever on a further expedition against Spain and died soon afterwards. The whole village went into mourning at the loss of such a heroic young life.

Gilbert the next son, frail even as a child, lived not to see his seventeenth birthday. Only two males remained to carry the Rudhall line, John and William. As boys, they fought constantly according to my grandmother, a situation that as a child, I confess I found somewhat comforting.

William Rudhall (c1549-1609) = Margaret dau. Sir James Croft

|

1. *Frances (b.c1575) = Herbert Westfaling*
2. *Richard Rudhall knighted at Cadiz (c1577-1601)*
3. *Gilbert Rudhall (c1579-1598)*
4. *Anne (b.c1582) = Thomas Price of The Priory*
5. *Joane (c1584-1625) = Sir Walter Pye of the Mynde*
6. *Joyce (c1585-1638) = Sir Samuel Aubrey of Clehonger*
7. *John Rudhall M.P. (c1587-1636) = Lady Choke dau Sir William Pitt*
8. *Margaret (d.c1589) = John Morgan of Llantilio Pertholey*
9. *William Rudhall, Royalist Army Colonel (c1591-1651)*
10. *Katherine (b.c1595) = Richard Broughton of Owlebury, Salop*
11. *Mary (c1596-1669)*

Salt & Silk

John Rudhall, the eldest son, married Lady Choke the daughter of Sir William Pitt and became a Member of Parliament and High Sheriff of the county. One day, while attending the Spring Assizes, he caught gaol fever, sickened and died, as did his three little daughters. Before he expired, he conveyed all his other manors and estates, those not included in his marriage settlement, to his sister Mary in trust – to spite his brother, who should have been the next to inherit them.

The youngest and now only surviving son William Rudhall became head of the family yet without having possession of all the estates. Even though I was only young when I first heard the story, I remember thinking what an intolerable position in which to find oneself! I was a second son. Samuel, my father's heir always took precedence and was given special treatment and for this I detested him.

What if he died and what if my father did the same thing to me and conveyed Clehonger and Dorstone to Anne? or Elizabeth? – even Mary? I never understood how Colonel Rudhall, as he later became during the Troubles, could conduct himself with such dignity under such unhappy circumstances in which God had placed him.

Frances, the oldest of the Rudhall sisters, married Herbert Westfaling the Bishop's son and lived at Mansell Gamage. My parents always talked of Great-Aunt Frances in hushed and sympathetic tones. Anne soon discovered why. Her husband, although a virtuous and kindly man, was busily consuming a large part of his estate in fanciful projects, all of which failed his expectations.

Instead of following in the footsteps of his esteemed father and grandfather and entering into the Church, he sincerely believed that he could give the world the benefit of his ingenious ideas and make it, if not a spiritually better place, then a happier one.

He pursued each invention in turn with a great tenacity of purpose, always assuring his wife that her many pounds that he was obliged to use in the development of his inventions, would come back to her an hundred-fold. In the course of his endeavours, he sold most of his estates and as a result of all this, Great-Aunt Frances could only watch helplessly as her fortune steadily diminished and their debts rapidly mounted.

At one time, he concentrated on the building of a levitation chamber with a flow of air from one end of an inner shroud to the other, causing the person so ensconced inside, to rise upwards. Unfortunately, not even the many bellows and hands to pump them could defy God's law that gave the power of flight only to birds.

Then came the combined night lamp and earth quake sensor, though to our limited knowledge, the land had not moved since God brought down his wrath on the evils of Sodom and Gomorrah. Only Great-Uncle Herbert's circular chessboard met with a degree of success; even then our grandfather complained that playing chess with his brother-in-law on such an outlandish design always gave him a headache and distracted him from the game.

The next daughter Joane married Sir Walter Pye of the Mynde, Attoney-General of the Court of Wards and Liveries, a court that our great Tudor monarch King Henry VIII had established to determine cases arising from disputes concerning the property of minors. At the time, Sir Walter was reputed to be the richest man in England. Great-Aunt Joane gave her husband fifteen children and was particularly close to our grandmother, and in turn to our own family.

Of the other daughters, Anne married Thomas Price of The Priory in Hereford. My father was particularly proud of the fact that their son Herbert Price, his cousin, entered the service of Queen Henrietta Maria and married one of her maids of honour. The King knighted him and he later represented Brecknock, the birthplace of our great-grandfather Morgan Aubrey. The next daughter Margaret married John Morgan of Llantilio Pertholey and Katherine, who wed late in life, married Richard Broughton of Owlebury.

Even though quite little, I remember my Grandmother Rudhall as being a stern and upright woman with grey hair piled high under her coif to whom my grandfather would defer on even the slightest matter. She and Great-Aunt Joane, who died before I was born, were considered gentlewomen of great sobriety and such paragons of womanly virtue, that they were once called upon to tame one of the Scudamore daughters, a member of Herefordshire's most distinguished family to whom we were distantly connected. When pressed to reveal the details of this story, my grandmother said that the young miss had more need of a good marriage than a new fashioned gown – a lesson I reminded my sisters they should heed.

In spite of differences in age and circumstance and character, my father's Rudhall cousins and he were all united in a common belief – and that was that the King was ordained by God to rule over his people, just as we know that God in Heaven rules over the whole universe and the Great Chain of Being.

On our visits to Rudhall Manor, we older children were usually given permission to explore the rambling old house with its cellars, its outhouses and surrounding gardens. We would play hide-and-go-seek, a game that Samuel hated because we made sure he could never find us.

Then our Great-Aunt Mary Rudhall would hear his cries and come seeking him out. She would comfort him and give him sugared plums 'to wipe away the tears'. I remember her as a little old woman with piercing blue eyes. Never having married, our grandmother's youngest sister bestowed particular affection on her many nieces and nephews and their children.

The son of one, Herbert Westfaling, the fourth of that illustrious name, became a close and trusted friend and exerted a great influence over me, and in all modesty, I over him.

12. The New Heir

My mother, a tall and commanding women, grew up in London, the daughter of Mathew Bedell, and his second wife Anne Boothby. Both families had prospered as Merchant Taylors. Mathew Bedell was a wealthy and pious man and held the position of Warden of the Merchant Taylors' Company in 1620. He later distinguished himself as an Alderman of the City of London.

I learnt through snippets of conversation and sometimes raised voices, that my mother's father Mathew Bedell had paid my grandfather £1,500 as my mother's marriage portion. She also brought with her into our family, the manors of Ford, Newton, Warton and Marston in Herefordshire and a residence with its adjoining land in the city of Hereford they called the Friars. In addition, my grandfather enjoyed the rents from the manor of Lye in the county of Gloucester, and my father's younger brother Anthony received an annuity of £30.

Such were the crumbs left for a younger son if he were lucky enough to be included in the marriage settlement of a son and heir. It led me to wonder, when I became conscious of such matters, what grains would be left to me when it came to my brother Samuel's turn to marry.

In a devoted and fruitful marriage, my mother bore a succession of children, the eldest being Anne named for our mother's mother and then Samuel, named for our father's father. Our parents always granted my brother special consideration, being the heir apparent, something that from my earliest memories I resented. The fact that one day he would inherit the manors of Clehonger and Dorstone and our other properties made him arrogant and his frequent

> Herbert Aubrey = Elizabeth Bedell
> (1603-1671)   (1609-1676)
> |
> 1. Anne (b.1629) = William Boothby
> 2. Samuel Aubrey (b.1630)
> 3. Herbert Aubrey (1631-1691) = Joyce Brydges
> 4. Mary (1632-1657)
> 5. Elizabeth (b.1633)
> 6. Mathew (b.1634)
> 7. Judith (b.c1635)
> 8. Godwin Aubrey (1636-1691) = Joan Clark
> 9. Thomas Aubrey (1637-1705)

sicknesses made him selfish and demanding.

Not being blessed with the most robust of health myself over the years, I can understand his feelings, but at the time, with the cruelty of children, we repaid this behaviour ten-fold by refusing him access to our games and by regularly teasing and tormenting him. When he could bear the distress no longer, he would burst into howls of tears and bring my mother running.

Even although God ordained me to be a second son, I proudly bore my father's name. Mary, the next eldest, liked to join in our games when we allowed her. She adored Anne and would follow her everywhere. Then came Elizabeth. She early developed into a protective little child and preferred to be with her mother after whom she was named, helping her with the babies, than to play with her older brothers and sisters.

My youngest sister Judith came soon after Mathew and was always the subject of concern on the part of my mother. I hardly remember little Mathew who caught a fever and moaned and suffered a long time before being carried off to God.

After that came Godwin and Thomas, the two youngest sons, whom we considered far too infantile to join in our games.

When our parents married, Sir Samuel and Lady Aubrey went to live in Greyfriars, a residence in one of the old monastic communities just outside Hereford's city walls that were sold to local gentry following the dissolution of the monasteries. The building had been split into two parts but it still gave plenty of room for our family to stay there, which we liked to do, especially during the long winter months.

I remember when visiting our grandparents, Anne and I would play hide-and-go-seek in the old convent orchard and stables, squealing with laughter and excitement when Samuel and the other children failed to find us. We would pick apples pretending they were windfalls, and I can still smell the wonderful aromas coming from the bake house.

One cloud hovered over our otherwise happy horizon and it became a leitmotif that persisted throughout my life. At the time of course it meant little to me, wrapped as I was in the secure love and protection of my parents.

From the time we were very little, our grandfather and father were constantly engaged in a war of words, and we soon learned that money, or the lack of it, was the chief topic of their disputes. To our dear mother's distress, every meeting of the two men resulted in raised voices. Sometimes we could not but hear snatches of their discord; other times, Anne, showing a curiosity unbecoming in a woman, would listen to them arguing behind closed doors.

No matter in whose presence he found himself, our grandfather constantly complained that he had so few rents on which to live. We knew he had sold the Sign of the Black Swan in London, the house his parents had always lived in, soon after his mother's death, and the lease of Shelwyke that our great-grandfather Morgan had bought just before he died, had also gone. Why he sold them, we never learnt, but Anne, in whose eyes our grandfather could do no wrong, claimed he did it to pay his debts.

My father wanted to know why our grandfather had not paid his creditors who were always sorely pressing him for the repayment of the loans he had taken out – and the interest. No answer to this repeated question ever satisfied my father.

Nor could my grandfather easily find the annual rent of £4 a year that had to be distributed to the poor of Llanfrynach, our great-grandfather Morgan Aubrey's old parish, for ever. This he seldom, if ever, paid on time. His tardiness in this matter was a constant topic of recrimination and in my father's eyes, a betrayal of filial trust and a lapse he never ceased to remind our grandfather.

Anne would regale us children with these accounts, thrilled that she could display her knowledge of such grown up matters. I would never stoop to such subterfuge as eavesdropping and I was not displeased when one day my father stormed out of the room having argued at length with my grandfather and caught Anne listening and gave her a strapping for her pains.

There existed one financial drain on both their resources on which they, and in fact all our cousins and neighbours met on common ground and that was the Ship Money[1]. Anne explained that each parish had to contribute the means to furnish one ship of three hundred and fifty tons for the safeguard of the seas and the defence of the realm. His Majesty had ordered this tax to be raised and in my eyes, such being a royal command then nobody should harbour treacherous thoughts against the King by complaining of it.

In spite of this, we had a happy enough childhood at Clehonger. We were oblivious to the significance of our grandfather's financial worries. We had been born and bred to believe that as landowners our tenants paid us money – and sometimes kind as well – and that the earth they worked and tilled and harvested belonged to us. On one occasion I overheard by chance my father shouting that Dorstone yielded £120 and Clehonger £82 in annual rent. I knew a hundred bushels of rye came to us each year, so with all that money coming in rent, we were secure. I assured Anne on this point and told her that when a gentleman needed money, he simply borrowed it.

One day I awoke to a strange silence in the house and found my father standing at the foot of my bed, staring at me. Samuel, who had been ailing again, had been moved to another chamber. His voice breaking, my father told me that Samuel had gone to God and now I had to fill his shoes as the son and heir, young as I was.

I knew not what to say and I remember it took me a little time to fully understand the significance of his words. I would never see Samuel again and all the hidden wishes that I had dared not even put into words in my mind had miraculously been granted. My childish body suddenly burned and then just as quickly, froze. The Devil had read my thoughts! My father said nothing, but simply looked hard at me while I blinked back my tears.

I could only assuage my guilt with a promise to God that I would pray for my brother's soul every night of my life. Now a new duty called and I resolved to fulfil the role so as to justify my father's faith in me. When the time came in the far distant future, I would confidently succeed him as the second Herbert Aubrey of Clehonger, Esquire.

***

Periodic crises punctuated the first ten years or so of my life, each one casting a greater gloom over the one before. Prices for corn and cattle fell, frost killed the spring growth, sickness broke out again in the county; a close neighbour succumbed to the fever, leaving his family destitute – all causing despair to my dear mother, who sent succour and comfort to the afflicted whenever she could.

But over and above the forlorn state of the countryside, one subject occupied my father and his friends most: yet another compulsory payment to the government of Ship Money. It provoked endless discussions and as young as we were, we could not but grasp its gravity.

This latest imposition caused great hardship throughout the county, for many people found they had no means to pay it. When this happened, the Sheriff ordered his constables to seize their goods and chattels. Sometimes the men disobeyed orders and refused to do so and as a consequence, the constables themselves were thrown into prison.

Worse still, some families who had to pay the tax were dealt a double blow by being struck down by the pestilence, in many cases leaving children orphaned and penniless. I often wondered what sins these people must have committed to have incurred the wrath of God with such severity.

Anne gave me her unasked opinion, as she often did on matters that caught her fancy. To her mind, both those who had refused to pay the Ship Money because of their circumstances and the 'poor constables' as she described them, were to be pitied and the latter had been unfairly punished. I reminded her that an order was an order and it had to be obeyed no matter what the circumstances. The money went to buy ships to defend our shores and we were born to obey our Sovereign Lord without a murmur of complaint.

My father now talked freely to me about the Tax, gratified that I appeared to understand its implications. I sympathised with him and all those other poor people who found themselves in such financial difficulties. I remember my response bringing a faint smile to his lips.

One immediate concern that my dear mother expressed at that time, was the fact that her father, Mathew Bedell, had taken a third wife. She learnt that he had just married Elizabeth Bird at St Gregory by St Paul in London. Although happy for him, she feared the acrimony among his children that would inevitably arise as a result of this extra partitioning of his estate. Young I was at the time, nobody could have foreseen that it would be I who would eventually be penalised as a result of my Grandfather Bedell's will.

In 1638 our upright and austere grandmother Lady Aubrey succumbed to the illness that also swept through Ross that year, when over three hundred fell victim to the plague. As my father's son and heir, I went with my parents to Hereford pay our last respects and arrived in time to see the 'sin eater', a lean wretch, ragged and salivating, ready and eager to participate in the age-old ritual of eating and drinking the sins of the dead.

The Cathedral church of Hereford was filled with our Rudhall relations, our grandmother's brothers and sisters and their husbands and their offspring, the Westfalings, the Prices and the Pyes. I can remember my father supporting my dear grandfather, grief and sadness overtaking us, as we all filed into the old stone-flagged church in front of the other mourners. Beside Great-Uncle William Rudhall, the head of the family, stood his sister Mary, quietly weeping.

On my grandmother's instructions, one of her servants delivered over her dead body lying on the bier, a loaf of bread together with a bowl of beer and sixpence to the 'sin eater', who looked as if he sorely needed sustenance. The varlet accepted it all, agreeing to take upon himself all her sins she had committed on this earth, to free her from walking abroad after her death on nights of a full moon. Considering the uprightness of her character, I doubted she had need of this ancient ceremony.

Her epitaph, extolling her many virtues, can be seen in the Cathedral, in spite of its desecration at the hands of the heathen hordes that later rampaged through that place of Christian worship. It reads:

> *Could dull words speak what buried here doth lie,*
> *'Twould raise both Envy and Idolatry.*
> *'Twas an Exchequer, throng'd with so much good,*
> *The age that lost it, never understood.*
> *Just heaven finding 'twas but envied here,*
> *Left us the Casket, fix'd the Jewel there.*

Of William Rudhall's seven daughters, only Mary remained, acting as a kind of matriarch to his many grandchildren.

---

1. Ship Money. This was levied to help fight the long and expensive war with Spain and Sheriffs were responsible for the entire collection from each county. Charles I spent most of the money so collected on naval improvements; even so, the levy proved to be extremely unpopular and was declared illegal in 1641.

13. Murder at Portadown

Hard on the heels of my grandmother's funeral came stories from London of the treasonable activities of the Puritan Parliamentarians. One in particular my father particularly detested, a Member by the name of John Pym[1] who was busy opposing the King's ministers and even confronting Archbishop Laud[2]. Merely the sound of his name brought a flush of rage to my father's face.

Then we heard the tales and slanderous accusations circulated about Queen Henrietta Maria[3]. Surrounded by Jesuits, they said she was actively encouraging Papists and worse still, secretly communicating with the rebellious Irish Catholics. Nothing would make me believe that His Majesty would ever allow his wife to indulge in such perfidious actions. We could only say special prayers for them both.

I remember in church one Sunday we were told to pray for the soul of the Earl of Strafford[4], the King's loyal adviser. He lost his head on Tower Hill to placate a hostile mob in London, where discontent had simmered to boiling point. Only blood would satisfy them. My father laid the blame for this outrage squarely at the foot of John Pym and his Parliamentary cohorts.

Such events, disconcerting as they were, seemed remote and far removed from our ordinary lives of learning our letters and sums, riding across the fields of wheat and rye, visiting the tenants with our father, and watching the hay being made.

Then the shadow of Parliament loomed ever larger over us. In London, Members signed what they called a Protestation. The document asserted the power and privilege of the body of Parliament, the lawful Rights and Liberties of the Subjects and of every Person making the Protestation.

At this, I have never seen my father so enraged, especially as it issued directions that everyone in the country should also sign it - from the Sheriffs and Magistrates down to all men eighteen years and over. Again my father and grandfather were as one when they learned of this treasonable and seditious act, as indeed were nearly all our neighbours, friends and kinsmen. Meetings were held on estates all over the county to discuss and sometimes argue what could be done to counter this treachery.

I can remember a particularly vociferous one conducted in our great parlour one afternoon. Among our visitors and loudest in his condemnation was a Cavalier of exemplary bravery, Sir Henry Lingen. We could not foresee it, but his courage and loyalty and that of our Uncle Anthony would soon be put severely to the test.

According to Anne, some of the other voices belonged to the High Sheriff Mr Fitzwilliam Coningsby and our father's cousins Colonel Herbert Price and Sir Walter Pye of the Mynde.

Eventually all were united and the result was our own 'Declaration or Resolution of the County of Hereford' drawn up in loyal support of His Majesty. The document bore nearly four thousand signatures of freeholders, inhabitants, knights, esquires, gentlemen of quality and ministers loyal to the Church of England. I only wished that I had been old enough to sign it as well.

I can still remember the autumn of 1641. I was about ten years old. We had celebrated the Festival of St Michael and All Angels and the tenants had come to pay their rents and present my father with the traditional goose. The nights were drawing in, the trees were turning, and Anne and I were already talking about what we could expect for Christmastide.

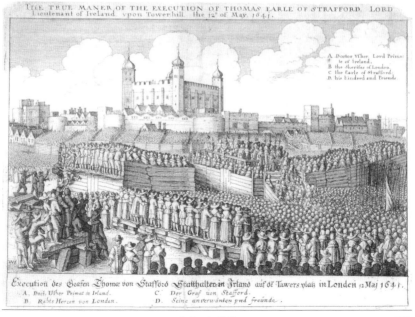

One evening, our father told us to remain behind in the withdrawing room after evening prayers, the time when we would try to squeeze in one last game before we were packed off to bed. The servants curtseyed and bowed and would have left the room, but he bade them stay, all save Sally whom he directed to take Anne and her sisters upstairs. Their sex and their years meant they were too tender to hear what he had to say. Anne's protests fell on deaf ears, but I suspected she would soon escape custody and be listening outside the door.

'I have terrible tidings to impart,' were the first words he used, before relating the awful sequence of events. I noticed his hands were shaking. 'My dear brother, your Uncle Morgan is dead, butchered at the hands of an Irish mob.'

The disbelief and stunned silence that met his words soon found their echo in the village, in the city of Hereford and indeed all over England. All too soon, rumours and tales gathered pace and swept the country. My father knew only that my uncle had been paying a visit to his friend Mr Fullerton, the minister of Loughhall, when sparked by who knows what, a murderous hoard gathered and drove the Protestants of Loughall, English and Irish alike, towards the bridge at Portadown.

Neither he nor our uncle, nor Mr Madder the minister of the parish of Donochmore, nor Mr New his curate, escaped. On that fateful twenty-third day in October in the year of Our Lord 1641, before the sun had set, they and hundreds of others: men, women and even children were hacked death on the bridge and cast into the bloody river below.

My mother refused to believe that Christian, God-fearing people could ever perpetrate such atrocities and directed that the family go into mourning immediately. My father ended that unforgettable evening by informing us, as he had done so many times before, that the Irish were uncivilised and that only the influence of the Protestant settlers, encouraged by His Gracious Majesty, could save the Irish from barbarism.

During the uprising, thousands of other Protestants were killed and the number of supposed victims and the terrible horrors to which they were subjected, grew with each new account until the whole beggared belief. Stories circulated that women and children were stabbed with pitchforks, cuts with swords and had been left to die, wallowing in their blood.

My father heard that Lady Fanshawe, in the country at the time, was awakened one night by an apparition in the form of a red haired woman in white who came to her casement window and moaned a warning of dire deeds to come. After the event, one twilight a ghost appeared in the water near the bridge in the form of a woman standing waist high in the water with dishevelled hair and closed hands held high crying, 'Revenge! Revenge!'

Some time later, in a dark mood which often settled over his countenance after these dire events, my father told us that it was to his brother Morgan that their grandmother had bequeathed her husband's gold ring with the Aubrey arms graven upon it.

'His ring should have come to me, my father's eldest son – not to my brother, but then he was named Morgan, not I. Who knows where my grandfather's ring is now? Into whose Irish hands has the gold fallen, that should have been mine? It's an ill, ill omen!'

After that, any idea of Roman Catholicism in general, and the Irish Catholics in particular, only confirmed and magnified my worst fears, and I vowed to resist such heretical beliefs no matter what the cost. I prayed also that my father's foreboding was only the result of grieving over a lost brother.

My poor grandfather never recovered from the shock of losing a beloved son, especially since his other son, my Uncle Anthony Aubrey, was already talking of joining Sir Henry Lingen's Horse. Anne in her womanish way did her best to comfort our grandfather on the occasions that presented such an opportunity. The old man now rambled when he spoke, slurring his words that made him well-nigh unintelligible at times. Not to Anne however, who repeated one of his outpourings to me in the strictest confidence.

Our grandfather, together with Richard Bevan his tenant in Dorstone and Lewis Powell a yeoman, had borrowed £150 from John Pauntlaw and a woman called Margaret Wigmore. As well, he got £10 from Bevan. Then a man called Peter Wyatt lent our grandfather £30, he being in necessitous circumstances at the time. His old friend John Powell stood surety for him for £60 as a guarantee that six months later he would repay Wyatt the £30 with £1-4s interest. 'I'll pay them all before I die, I swear before God,' he told Anne.

Although the finer points of these financial transactions escaped me,

I assured my sister that she should have no fears on that score: a gentleman always borrowed money when the need arose, especially when their tenants were behind in their rents or were lazy and inefficient.

A year after my uncle's murder, the summer of 1642 seemed to us children, one just like any other, but ominous rumours filtered through to Hereford, concerning Members of Parliament who were now actively opposing His Majesty.

Then news came that King Charles had raised his standard at Nottingham, and a proclamation had been read, denouncing the House of Commons and their troops as traitors. At that my father became very agitated, more so when we heard that many of his friends vowed to raise troops at their own expense to support the Royal cause. A gloom settled over Clehonger Manor and the whole village.

We were on the threshold of events that none of us, living in such a remote and peaceful corner of England, could have possibly foreseen. All over the county that summer, friends and kinsmen were raising military forces in preparation for war. My father's cousin Sir Walter Pye of the Mynde, a fearless man and Royalist to the core, headed these activities, followed by Lord Scudamore who was busy collecting arms and ammunition at his seat of Holme Lacy with which to arm his followers.

Somehow, the county raised £3,000 and sent it to the King at York. Then news came that the Queen had sailed from Pendennis for Holland to raise troops and supplies for the Royalist cause and had taken the crown jewels with her – for safekeeping, they said. Anne and I, in agreement for once, decided we would much rather prefer the treasure fall into foreign hands than into those of Parliament.

1. John Pym (?1584-1643) M.P. and bitter critic of the government. He directed the setting up of administrations to support the war against Charles and worked to pursue alliance with the Scots.

2. William Laud (1573-1645), Archbishop of Canterbury. He was determined to impose conformity on the Church of England and demanded savage penalties on those who opposed him. He was an obvious target for revenge, and when Charles's regime collapsed, he was imprisoned, impeached, and executed.

3. Henrietta Maria (1609-1669) Queen of England. After a cool start to her marriage to Charles, their relationship turned to devoted love. Her Catholicism fuelled fears that she was unduly influencing her husband to promote Catholic interests. She moved to France in 1644 and after Charles' execution, she was left poverty-stricken.

4. Thomas Wentworth, 1st Earl of Strafford (1593-1641) politician and influential supporter of King Charles I. When the King fell from power, he abandoned Strafford, and assented to his attainder or automatic conviction of treason. He was subsequently executed in 1641.

14. War without an Enemy

For the next few weeks my father made us all stay in doors and told the servants to bring in whatever harvest produce still remained and store what they could in the cellars. He also laid in a stock of weapons, petronels and carbines, the latter being a smaller pistol he considered of more use. The idea of firing one greatly excited my little brothers. My father did his best to allay the fears of our tenants and we could only wait and say our prayers and ask God to protect us all.

The prospect of our brave Royalist soldiers putting all the traitorous Puritans to the sword came to life in a new game for us children. I always played the part of the King and I relegated Anne to the role of Parliament. I remember this caused great friction; not even Mary, and certainly not Elizabeth, wanted to be on Anne's side.

But then word came that the Roundheads, as we came to call them, under the command of the Earl of Stamford[1] with a detachment of nine hundred men, three troops of horse and two pieces of ordnance had entered the city of Hereford. They conquered it easily, meeting little or no resistance; some said because many armed Royalists refused to join battle. Hearing this, we realised that the Puritans were in fact very close to home and we ceased our feuding and childish pastimes.

Stamford's soldiers plundered indiscriminately and remorselessly and word came to us that they threatened to keep us so short of food that we would be forced to eat the very flesh from our arms. The Commander took up residence in the Bishop's palace and many people were compelled to billet soldiers in their houses. They had little hope of any recompense for the expense involved.

Then we heard that my grandfather had been forced to quarter a number of Puritan troops at Greyfriars. My father paled at this news, knowing that it meant a further drain on our grandfather's dwindling resources, made all the worse by the fact that Sir Samuel had still not paid his creditors.

Our dear mother pacified my father's distress and tried to keep matters normal as she gave the servants more duties and continued teaching us our letters and numbers. Then we heard that houses had been looted in the city, and in the countryside a company of Parliament soldiers had plundered Mr Geers' house at Garnons, six miles from Hereford, and had taken horses, money and linen. Daily we waited for the sound of horses thundering up to our house, followed by a threatening bang on the doors, but for this time at least, Clehonger Manor and our tenants were spared.

Royalists were strengthening their forces at the Mynde, under the energetic leadership of Sir Walter Pye, leaving the Earl and his Puritan followers in the city very vulnerable. To our relief, Earl Stamford and his Parliamentary troops were ordered to retreat.

The Parliamentarians all fled from Hereford and at last we felt safe – until a troop of Royalist soldiers descended on us, looking for traitors. In vain my father proclaimed our loyalty to His Majesty, but they heeded him not and took some pewter and plate and some of my mother's best linen - for good measure, they stated. My father said they were welcome to it, but my mother had to be comforted for some time after they had left.

The memory of those Royalist soldiers plundering our possessions as if we had aided and abetted the enemy, stayed with me for many years. After they had gone, Elizabeth helped our mother hide whatever chattels they could and the house remained quiet. Anne and I no longer played our games, but talked to each in whispers and wondered what next was in store for us.

Those people who had in fact aided the occupying army were brought to Hereford and denounced as traitors. They were all suitably punished and some were put into the Bishop's prison to remind them where their loyalties should lie.

At last we felt safe with Hereford in the hands of the Royalists and Fitzwilliam Coningsby of Hampton Court as Governor of the city and garrison. In spite of that, yet another demand tested the loyalty of many. The county was ordered to raise £3,000 a month for the King's needs. At this news, my father fell into yet another slough of despond. Not even Anne's cheerful disposition could lift his worried expression.

The next year's spring flowers were starting to appear when a further disaster, or rather series of disasters, speedily befell us. We heard that the Parliamentary general Sir William Waller[2] had taken Farnham Castle and Arundel Castle and had even captured Chichester. Now he and his army were marching towards Hereford.

Once again we told our tenants to prepare for the worst and waited anxiously for news. Some days elapsed while Clehonger held its collective breath, as did the people of Hereford. We later heard what happened inside the city.

Just before dawn on the morning of the twenty-fourth day of April, the guard on sentry duty noticed a series of movements in the distance and immediately roused the Governor from his bed. Through the morning mist, Sir Richard Cave could just make out the enemy approaching, their steel headgear glinting in the early light. Sir William Waller and his men were less than a mile from the walls. Sir Richard at once ordered trumpets and drums to sound, to alert his troops to come running from their lodgings and report to their posts. To his despair, Sir Richard found he could only muster his own weak foot regiment and a few gentlemen volunteers, among them Lord Scudamore and my grandfather, to make up a garrison to defend the city.

Finding it impossible to hold the city walls effectively with such a meagre force at his command, in desperation, the Governor requested a parley with the Parliamentarians. Sir William Waller agreed and called a cease-fire. The two men met and took some hours to negotiate the terms – which fortunately allowed most of the Royalist infantry to escape over the walls with their weapons.

Sir William drew up Articles for the Surrender of the City of Hereford and imposed a series of conditions to which Sir Richard was forced to agree. My father was pleased to learn that the proclamation directed that all ladies and gentlewomen were to have honourable usage. The Bishop and Dean and others were to be free from attack on their persons and their goods were not to be plundered.

Even so, Sir Richard was forced to pay £3,000 to restrain the Roundheads from plundering the town. And Sir William purloined enough plate to fill five trunks, which he sent to London to be coined and returned to pay his troops. Once again, the citizens of Hereford were compelled to give officers and their troops free quarter, which we knew would be an additional drain on my grandfather's slender means. We had heard nothing from him for days but he was constantly in our prayers.

To allay our uncertainty, or so I thought, my father summoned us all into the great parlour – even the servants - and I could see from his face that he had grave news to impart.

'The Puritans have apprehended about a dozen Royalists of consequence in Hereford', he began, 'and I am told they have been transported to Bristol.' As we listened in silence, he gave us their names. It read like roll call of our kinsmen.

'Commander of the garrison Sir Richard Cave, Lord Scudamore, his lady and his son James, (I remember my mother gasping in astonishment when she heard these names uttered), High Sheriff of the county Fitzwilliam Coningsby and his son Humphrey, Sir Walter Pye, Sir William Croft, the Governor of the City Colonel Herbert Price and his father Lieutenant Colonel Thomas Price....', he paused. 'And one we hold most dear in our hearts - my father Sir Samuel Aubrey.' Anne let out a wail of anguish.

'Let us pray for the safety of all of them. Dear Lord, hear our prayer....' My father's voice wavered as I bowed my head and followed his words of supplication.

---

1. Stamford, Henry Grey, 1st Earl (?1599-1673), West Country Parliamentary General. He changed sides and declared for the King in 1659, resulting in his imprisonment in the Tower until the Restoration.

2. Sir William Waller (1598-1668), M.P. and successful Parliamentary General. It was he who called the conflict 'this war without an enemy'.
   In 1652 he married as his third wife, Lady Anna the daughter of William Lord Paget; their great-granddaughter, the Hon. Arabella Harcourt married Herbert Aubrey II's grandson Herbert Aubrey IV.

15. Frontline Hereford

After that, my memories blurred into a sequence of nightmares, some when awake and many when asleep. I remember my little brothers ceased their childish squabbles, which worried my mother who feared they might be ailing. Even the servants went about their duties in silence; it was as if a pall had descended over the whole house. Every day we waited for news from Bristol, praying for it to be relieved, but it remained securely in enemy hands.

Then to our relief, we learned that the Governor, Sir Richard Cave had escaped from captivity, Colonel Herbert Price had been exchanged and Sir Walter Pye ransomed and released. Unhappily, our grandfather still languished in Bristol, imprisoned with the other Royalist captives.

He was constantly in our prayers and God answered them, for not long afterwards, our wonderful Prince Rupert captured Bristol and our grandfather and all the rest of the prisoners who had been taken from Hereford, were freed.

That is, all save one, Lord Scudamore, to whom we were proud to claim kinship. Being the brave and ardent Royalist he was, on hearing of Sir William Waller's advance on Hereford, he had betaken himself from Holme Lacy, his seat, to Hereford and put himself under Sir Richard Cave's orders. After the capitulation of the city and his arrest, the Puritans released him on condition he submit himself to Parliament in London.

Once there, his troubles began. The Parliamentarians kept him in confinement for nearly four years, while his goods were seized and his houses and their contents destroyed. Those effects that escaped the looters' hands were sold and the proceeds employed for the forces under the command of Sir William Waller, by then ensconced in Gloucester. My Lord's pleas to Parliament for redress and justice fell on deaf ears.

In the meantime, Prince Rupert's capture of Bristol and his successful movements south ensured that Royalists once more had control of Hereford. My father brought us news that Sir Henry Lingen had been appointed Sheriff and that Sir Richard Cave was to be court-martialled on charges of giving up the city dishonourably.

I remember my mother demanding to know how poor Sir Richard

could have done ought else to defend the city against the numbers behind Sir William Waller, given the paucity of troops at his disposal. 'In any case, I believe them both to be honourable men.' My father could only shake his head, relieved as we all were that the enemy had flown and we were now safe once again. But uppermost in our minds was our concern for my dear grandfather. How had he survived his captivity?

Anne was overjoyed to see him, as we all were, when he slowly dismounted at the door of Clehonger Manor at last. The servants lined up to pay their respects and my two younger brothers almost knocked him over as they rushed to greet him. The welcome brought a faint smile to his gaunt face. His captivity had taken its toll, because as young as I was, I remember noticing his beard was now almost white and he seemed to have shrunk in height.

They treated us... well enough... but the food... I'm much relieved... but the money..' Anne listened attentively to his rambling and repetitious utterances until he fell asleep in his chair. She reported to me that money was at the forefront of his concerns. Sir William Waller had indeed instructed that his prisoners be used honourably, but he had ordered that householders pay £40 in lieu of having their houses plundered. We knew that my grandfather still had many of his debts to settle, nevertheless, our relief at his survival overcame these petty considerations.

Hereford now rested securely in Royalist hands after having twice been taken by the Parliamentarians, and so as to counter any future threat to the city, His Majesty gave the new Governor of Hereford, Colonel Barnabas Scudamore, Lord Scudamore's younger brother, authority to fortify the city with whatever means he could. As a start, he demanded contributions from those citizens who could afford to pay, which meant that my father and grandfather were both liable and our circumstances were even further reduced.

One day, a young officer and a troop of soldiers galloped up to our door and demanded that they be given free quarter. My father arranged for a number of the soldiers to be billeted with our tenants, and promised the latter he would compensate them for the financial losses incurred. For the rest of the men, we were obliged to accommodate them for a time at the manor house. My mother bore this imposition with great dignity, and being Royalist soldiers, they were polite enough and knew their place.

One of them, a tall farmer's son from Gloucestershire, as I remember, spent whatever time he could in the kitchen, talking to Sally. I supposed that he was trying to impress her with tales of his military campaigns, although I failed to comprehend why such a topic could interest a servant wench.

Godwin and Thomas were now old enough to ask incessant questions and importuned him at every opportunity to show them his weapons and how they were loaded, which they complained to me that he always resisted. By chance, I was present on one of these occasions and demanded that he give such an instruction, and that he should teach me and that I should take precedent, being my father's son and heir. I swore to attend to his words as if my life depended on it, which indeed it might well have and commanded that the lesson begin.

The man took his musket and handed it to me with a ready enough smile, but its weight was more than I expected it to be. He quickly rescued the precious weapon from its near crash to the ground and Thomas rudely laughed. My clip over his ear immediately turned that sound into screams.

Continuing the lesson, my instructor took the required amount of gunpowder from his bandalier and carefully poured it into the barrel of the musket, making sure not to spill any and packed it in hard with a stick. Then he put in the lead ball and pressed it into place with a piece of wadding. I quickly grasped the intricacies of loading the weapon and swore to use one against the Roundheads, just as soon as I was old enough to bear its weight.

My grandfather could not return to Greyfriars. As it lay outside the city gates, and close enough to give cover to any invading army, the Governor had ordered the old building to be demolished. Anne wept when she heard what had happened, and I too felt the loss, knowing that our childhood days there would never return. In spite of Anne's tears and pleading, our grandfather refused come to Clehonger and live with us. Even at that tender age, I remember being aware that our father's antagonism towards our grandfather had increased in intensity and their heated arguments always involved tenants and rents and debts.

So instead, the old man collected what possessions he could from Greyfriars and went to live in the Widow Hill's house in Hereford. Who the Widow Hill was, I never discovered, but my parents would always look at each other whenever her name was mentioned. I supposed at least she would care for him more readily and in better comfort than we could provide.

Some of the stones from Greyfriars were removed to help fortify Hereford castle. I went with my father and some men to retrieve other building materials and whatever else we could find from my grandfather's old residence. We rightly determined they belonged to us and we would save them for future use at Clehonger.

One day an officer with a troop of men arrived with orders from Sir Barnabas Scudamore that they remove all the lead from our roof that they could transport and whatever iron implements they could find. My parents could only watch helplessly as day after day they saw a part of Clehonger Manor taken apart and trundled way – all to aid in the fortification of the city of Hereford.

After they had taken their fill, my father arranged for workmen to make secure from the elements what remained of the house and promised to pay them handsomely as soon as the troubles were over. I remember my mother being often in tears at this time, while we children and the servants tried to adjust ourselves to our depleted surroundings.

Our grandfather's imprisonment, the death of his wife, the murder of his son and the destruction of Greyfriars – not to mention his constant financial worries - contributed to his many ills, but he did not long have to suffer them. He died at the Widow Hill's house on the sixteenth day of May in the Year of our Lord 1645, a sad and unhappy man, estranged from his sister and at odds with his son, as he himself was, when young, with his own father, my great-grandfather Morgan Aubrey.

We buried him in the Cathedral Church of Hereford next to our grandmother. His epitaph read:

> *He who did never lodge within his breast*
> *Dishonour, Baseness or Selfe Interest,*
> *The just man's Friend, the poor man's Treasure,*
> *The oppress'd Man's Patron in extremity;*
> *Lies here (Reader) if now thou grudge a Tear,*
> *Find some more worthy object, spend it there.*

> *Vita et Morte: Concordes Conjuges Samuelis et Jocosa Aubrey*
> *hic jacent.*

Anne cried the most and could not be consoled for days. Many of his old friends mourned him and one in particular, John Powell, called him a friendly neighbour and a gentleman well beloved. He had been a Justice of the Peace and had always upheld the Aubrey name. I was proud that he had served his King with such dignity.

As for my poor father, he now had the additional worry of placating my grandfather's numerous creditors. My father sold what he could of my grandfather's effects, plate, horses, household stuff and the rest of his personal estate, which allowed him to repay £120 to John Pauntlow and Margaret Wigmore to whom he owed money.

One day another creditor, Peter Wyatt, came to Clehonger Manor and charged my father with dealing 'unnaturally' with Sir Samuel by not using the rents of Dorstone and Clehonger to pay his debts as my grandfather had promised him. Mr Wyatt threatened immediate court action. Through tears, Anne imparted these unhappy tidings to me, having overheard our father's heated denials to the charge. It took some time to calm her fears. We could only ask God to give our father strength and courage to meet these additional troubles.

Soon the Governor of Hereford faced a new and unexpected threat to the security of the city to whose fortification we had contributed so much. Waves of farmers and peasants from the neighbouring counties, numbering thousands, straggled towards the city. They called themselves Clubmen[1] and the leaders demanded to see the Governor whom they said would be sure to redress their grievances.

My father believed they had much justification, being ignorant and uninterested in the causes for which we were fighting. Battles had been waged over their land, in some cases more than once, and in consequence, troops of both sides had destroyed their property, purloined their produce and violated their womenfolk. Many threatened violence, and considering the huge numbers facing him, the Governor thought it wise to mollify them. He promised to do whatever he could to protect their interests to the extent that was in his power. This placated their leaders who bade the men continue on.

My father was very relieved to learn of this outcome, as numbers of them had wandered through Clehonger and the neighbouring countryside armed with shovels and pickaxes and crows of iron, demanding food from the cottagers. Many villagers had sympathised with their plight and gave what victuals they could, but at length the men dispersed peacefully.

1. Clubmen were local associations of civilians from all but the highest ranks of rural society where plundering and general depredation was the greatest. Their aim was to keep the war out of their localities and remain neutral. The movement spread from Worcestershire to the Welsh borders. They were ill-equipped and poorly trained and posed little to no threat to either side. Oliver Cromwell called them 'poor silly creatures'. .

16. The Siege

In the meantime, my father had insisted I return to the Hereford School, for although battles were still being fought across the country, he considered my education – as fragmented as it had been - too important to be longer neglected. Besides, as my father pointed out, His Majesty had directed that £4 a year be paid by the school to a scholar at Oxford. He expected me to be that scholar.

I went back to the School with mixed feelings, especially since I would be forced again into the traditional Spartan existence that I knew made men out of boys, which only a young and immature mind would doubt. The bell for Chapel rang at five every morning, then we spent the morning in the Library until ten when we ate dinner during which a Bible clerk would read from the Scriptures. We could converse with each other, when allowed, only in Latin and if our Master deemed us worthy, after a simple supper at five in the evening, we were permitted to play football for a short time in the College court.

We boys had to know our Catechism, the Psalter, the Book of Common Prayer and of course the Bible. These I excelled in, but I struggled with Lilly's Latin grammar and did my best with Ovid and Seneca. I often suffered the indignity of the birch in the hands of the Masters as a punishment for my inability to master the intricacies of arithmetic.

For nearly two years I lived in the closed world of scholarship, hardly aware of the fortunes of His Majesty for whom we prayed daily.

Only my time in the Chapel and reading the Good Book, gave me solace. So I heaved a secret sigh of relief when my father arrived unexpectedly at the School one day. He bade me return immediately with him to Clehonger. Lord Leven[1] and 14,000 Scotsmen were descending on Hereford.

We faced yet another terrible danger.

At Clehonger Manor, my mother hid what was left of our valuable plate wherever she could and ordered us to stay in the house at all times, while my father secreted our small stock of weapons and powder under a load of hay in one of our barns. We braced ourselves for the worst and my father alerted our tenants to do likewise. We could now only pray for deliverance and wait for the enemy to come.

The fortifications of the city that Governor Scudamore had put in place were soon put to the test, for almost at once we heard that the Scotsmen had completely surrounded the city. They expected instant capitulation, but the barbarians met a stronger resistance than they had anticipated. The Governor sent word to the Commander, the Earl of Leven, that he would surrender the city only by special order of His Majesty – which he had not been given - and so the siege of Hereford began.

Sure enough, the next morning just as dawn was breaking, we heard the familiar sound of horses thundering up to the manor house and a troop of bedraggled soldiers, a number lagging behind on foot, demanded food for themselves and fodder for their horses – and shelter. They were all well armed, those on horses had large petronels at the ready, so my father thought it wise to give in to their demands without resisting, even although he could hardly understand their fractured English.

The soldiers commandeered some of our remaining bedrooms, but it soon became apparent that food and money were uppermost in their minds, as their Commander was not providing them with enough of either. My father stood by, endeavouring to remain calm, as he watched them rampaging through the smith's shop, the dairy and store rooms and the workhouse, taking whatever they fancied. Outside, a party of them hacked down three of my mother's favourite elm trees while others took away what they could of our livestock.

My sister Anne and I hid in the priest's hole which had survived the Royalist soldiers' visitation, while all this took place. The Scots troops went through all the chambers upstairs, as our mother comforted Elizabeth and Mary and my little brothers as best she could. I can still hear their frightened screams and wails, as they clung to her skirts, not understanding what was happening.

The first evening they were there, my father insisted on us all gathering for prayers, and invited what soldiers were present, to join us. At first they were suspicious, but my father reassured them – astutely I thought – that we would be simply reading from the Good Book. They shuffled into the great parlour, and stood with heads bowed that first night, as my father read from St Paul's letter to the Corinthians. It became a nightly ritual.

One evening, a newcomer took his place among the men for evening prayers. At the conclusion, he stood forward and announced himself to be a lay Elder of the Scottish Church. He bade us 'Saxons' as he referred to us with a condescending smile, all retire, as he had need to give an additional lesson to 'these gud Covenenters'. Such was the name he gave the assembled soldiers.

My father bowed and acceded to his demand and bade us all retire. My curiosity being aroused as to the nature of this 'lesson', being ever attentive to Church ritual, I was forced to rely yet again on my sister Anne for this intelligence.

Unfortunately, the language in which the Preacher spoke, although loud, and the thickness of the door, prevented her from gleaning all but the essentials. She easily recognised the words 'looting', 'drinking' and 'swearing' but she confessed that she could not make out what he meant by his admonition, which he dealt with at some length, referring often in the process of his utterance to 'hell' and 'damnation', and against the evils of 'lying with loose women'. She determined to apply to our servant girl Sally for enlightenment.

For six weeks the siege dragged on, as the city withstood the onslaught. The Scots used Clehonger Manor as if they owned it, took whatever they wanted, ate our food and robbed our stores, but they never found our cache of weapons and powder – or the priest's hole where Anne and I had hidden some of our own treasures.

Every morning from first light, we would hear cannon fire from afar and could only pray that the Governor's fortifications of Hereford were holding firm against the constant bombardment. Then we would hear occasional screams and the neighing and whinnying of horses and the sounds of hooves galloping away into the distance.

From time to time I saw from the upper casements, wagons laden with the dead, the dying and the wounded, trundling past. Sometimes they would bring the injured into the house and Anne would help my mother staunch the blood and bandage their wounds. Such sights lifted my spirits, seeing evidence of God's wrath on these foreign interlopers.

One day, I ventured into one of the barns to retrieve my favourite slingshot that I had hidden there, thinking it would be safe to do so, when I noticed two people lying on the hay. One of them I recognised as our servant girl Sally, although her face was hidden by the head of the man with her. Neither of them saw me. I shall draw a veil over the scene, which I confided in no one, but it haunted me for many years afterwards. It reminded me that Anne had never again referred to the words of the lay Preacher.

Those six weeks seemed interminable, and all I could think of was being old enough to handle a musket and join Sir Henry Lingen's regiment with my Uncle Anthony, or be with Colonel Scudamore, the Governor of the city, holding out as they did, so bravely against the Scots army.

Then early one morning, both inside and outside our house, all seemed unnaturally quiet and to our great relief, there was not a Scottish soldier to be seen anywhere. It was as if they had simply melted away during the night. The men had taken most of our best horses and grain and other produce that was to see us through the coming winter, but nevertheless, the relief was immense. God had answered our prayers, and we knew that once more Hereford was secure in Royalist hands. The Scots army had retreated, taking their wounded but leaving behind their dead which amounted to two thousand men. The brave defenders of the city lost a mere twenty-one.

Then an event took place that made us forget our troubles. Soon after the Scots left, His Majesty entered Hereford in triumph. We children donned whatever good clothes we could find, short and tight and old as our breeches and jackets and bonnets had become, and rode with our parents to Hereford to be among the cheering crowds to welcome the King. Seated on his horse, proud and regal in a purple cloak, His Majesty bowed and waved his plumed hat. My hurrah was easily the loudest, and as he passed through the throng, he looked straight at me, caught my eye and smiled. For the whole of my life, I never forgot that moment.

The sun shone brightly that day for all of us, and particularly for our Governor, Barnabas Scudamore whom the King knighted. His Majesty even augmented the city's coat of arms, in gratitude of the defence of Hereford. It bore ten saltires to represent the ten Scottish regiments that had besieged the city and with it the motto: 'Reward for Invincible Loyalty'.

Winter came early that year, and I can remember that we were often hungry and nearly always cold, as the plunderers had taken most of our

Salt & Silk

stores and much of our wood that we had dried and stored. But little did we know that for our sins, Hereford would fall to the enemy for the third time in as many years, and that we would soon be visited by the Devil incarnate. As for me, when I came to man's estate, this villain came to be a living cross which I had to bear. My fear and hatred for him began then and has consumed me ever since.

***

Before continuing with this chronicle, I am duty bound to reveal everything I know about a man whose name would soon to strike terror into all our hearts. He and his barbarous hordes captured our city by deception and stealth without, and by treachery and duplicity within.

Even the very thought of him brought a sweat to my brow and a tremor to my whole being. Unhappily, our paths were to cross years after this most unhappy event that I am about to relate, so I feel I am more than qualified than most to draw a picture of this man. I refer of course to Colonel John Birch[2], in whose presence even powerful men were said to quail and none dared gainsay him.

He liked to boast of his humble origins, but never was there a more inept and false epithet to describe him or his beginnings. Arrogant, overbearing and acquisitive, yes – humble, never. A wine merchant from Bristol, he knew nothing of the meaning of loyalty – only to the lining of his own pocket.

He cared purely for himself, never for the tenets of Presbyterianism of which his father was said to be an Elder and in which guise he first came to the attention of Parliament. He persuaded them of his military prowess and they gave him a commission with the rank of Captain. Nor, as he later falsely claimed, did he harbour any latent belief in our King and the Established Church for which so many devout Royalists gave their lives.

The first weeks of that terrible December, when I first heard his name, far from introducing the Season of Joy and Thanksgiving for the birth of our Saviour, they launched the worst winter in living memory. Icy winds drove the snow across the countryside and the freezing cold crept into every corner of every house and hovel. The River Wye froze solid and cold and hunger ruled the land and carried off many in our village with it.

We children were almost always hungry. What stores were left, were rapidly dwindling. Our dear mother, always wrapped in layers of clothes, her fingers blue with cold, did what she could to ensure that at least we had a bowl of gruel each, after our nightly prayers.

Unbeknown to us, struggling to keep warm, four miles away, a group of Birch's men, dressed as labourers and pretending they were looking for work, tricked the sentry into opening Hereford's city gate. What human frailty lay behind such an action we shall never know; only that a murderous rabble of soldiers hiding nearby, stormed through the open gate and fell upon the innocent city – and captured it.

They streamed into the cathedral and knocked the heads off statues and damaged effigies on tombs. The Dean rushed into the pulpit, angrily protesting at such sacrilege, and would have been shot by one of the rioting soldiers, had not Birch himself rescued him.

In the confusion, and to our great relief, Sir Barnabas Scudamore fled across the icy waterway and was able to reach Ludlow. Sir Henry Lingen and my Uncle Anthony managed to make their escape across the frozen Wye to Goodrich Castle.

Naturally Colonel John Birch received the thanks of Parliament who paid him £6,000 for his men and made him Governor of the city. To our fury, he allowed Hereford to be plundered and the Roundheads took about eight hundred persons of quality prisoner and transported them to London. The city fell into a desperate state of lawlessness, with refuse heaped in the streets and beggars on every corner. The Governor declared martial law.

Once again, we were forced to stand by helplessly, as soldiers invaded our freezing house, ransacked our possessions, and took whatever caught their fancy. We were doubly unlucky, for one of the men, helping himself to some hay in our barn, found our hidden cache of weapons and powder. We were immediately charged with using our manor house as a garrison against Parliament.

In vain my father protested that they had never been used against any invader of our property, but the soldier at once confiscated the lot. He warned my father with a sneer that Colonel Birch did not take kindly to secretly armed Royalist sympathisers.

Then we suffered the indignity of having to quarter a company of troops, at least this time Englishmen, who left only after they had taken what little food and produce they could find, to the despair of my poor mother. My father promised our tenants that he would sue for compensation for all their losses as well, but he held out little hope for adequate recompense.

After escaping from Hereford, Sir Henry Lingen, the gallant Royalist related by marriage to Sir Walter Pye of the Mynde, together with my Uncle Anthony, made their way to Goodrich Castle, one of the last Royalist strongholds in the county. Thanks be to God, they survived to tell the tale. This garrison of Cavaliers upwards of a hundred strong knew all the intricate roads and passes that intersected the country and all the fords on the Wye. The castle withstood the onslaught for nearly four months.

During that time, it happened that a niece of Colonel Birch called Alice found herself caught in the precincts of the castle when the assault began. She had become enamoured of the son of a local Royalist commander and at the height of the siege, they decided to escape together, crossing the River Wye by the ford at Goodrich Boat. The dark waters of the swollen river claimed their lives and according to my Uncle Anthony, who related the story to me many years later, the ghosts of the lovers can be seen on stormy nights, still trying to complete their crossing.

The Royalists successfully held out against Birch and his troops until a rain of shots from a huge mortar piece breached the walls of the castle and resulted in such damage, that it fell to the enemy. Sir Henry marched out at the head of the defeated garrison, my uncle among them, to a rousing tune called 'Sir Henry Lingen's Fancy', waving his plumed hat in defiance, while his officers defiantly cried 'Harry for the King!'. We heard these news with mixed feelings. My father gathered us all together and announced that, God be praised, his brother had survived the onslaught and defeat of Goodrich Castle.

Unhappily, the Royalist stronghold of Oxford had also been forced to surrender to the Roundheads. The King had tried to escape capture, but without success. My mother and sisters cried at hearing such dismal tidings and I vowed that one day, I would take sword in hand and avenge myself on His Majesty's traitors. In spite of that, one ray of hope shone in the far distance: the Prince of Wales had fled the country – they said dressed as a woman – and had taken refuge in France. I said a special prayer for him every night.

1. Earl of Leven, Alexander Leslie, (1580-1661), veteran of the Thirty Years War, and leader of the Scottish army, the Covenanters. After the siege of Hereford he returned to Scotland where he was captured by a troop of English dragoons during Cromwell's 1651 invasion. He was imprisoned in the Tower for several years before returning to Fifeshire.

2. John Birch of Garnstone, co. Hereford (1616-1691) M.P. and Colonel in the Parliamentary Army. His nephew's granddaughter Elizabeth Morse married Herbert Aubrey II's great-grandson Harcourt Aubrey.

17. War's Aftermath

In those five years, from the time of our uncle's death on the bridge at Portadown, our lives had changed beyond anything we could have imagined. I saw sights that no child should witness, and for years afterwards, Mary would wake us all in the night, screaming in terror that the Scots had returned. I have to admit that even I experienced nightmares and had to be comforted by our wonderful mother who did all she could to see us through these horrors.

Such were the civil wars that I lived through as a child and a young man, when friend fought friend and kin fought kin. The world had turned topsy-turvey.

Our kinsman Sir Robert Pye, an ardent Royalist, garrisoned his mansion at Faringdon in Berkshire for the King, and was besieged there by his eldest son. To my father's fury, most of the St.Johns, the family of our Great-Aunt Katherine's third husband, sided with the Parliamentarians. One of them, Oliver St.John, a kinsman by marriage, fought on the side of the enemy, and died of wounds after the battle of Edgehill. Closer to home, and adding insult to injury, my mother's sister Mary took for her second husband, Lewis Audley, a Colonel in the Parliamentary army, a man I would later face in Court.

In spite of all the turmoil in our lives, our faith in God and the Established Church, never wavered. We prayed daily for our world to be put aright with the return our anointed Monarch, but we waited in vain. And as if God had not punished us enough for our sins, to add to our misery and deprivation, we were to endure years of failed harvests.

In the meantime, my father was to suffer yet another heavy blow.

One day, not long after we learnt of Sir Henry Lingen's surrender at Goodrich Castle and the defeat of the Royalist forces at Oxford, my father called me into his study. He rarely allowed us to into the room he called his own, and I could see at once that something was wrong. Papers lay in piles on the floor and the drawers of his cabinet gaped open. He sat sprawled behind his desk, his wig awry.

'I have grave tidings to impart,' he said, his voice shaking. 'The Committee for Compounding – and it has only just been formed – has sent me this.' He handed me a document with trembling hands. 'I have been fined the sum of £500, which amount the Roundheads claim to be one tenth the value of my estate.'

I could find no words, either on the page or in my mouth, to give the lie to this unhappy fact. 'They have charged me this sum, simply because they say I was on my estate when they claim that it had been held a garrison against Parliament! Yet we never fired a shot against the enemy, but we billeted their troops, while your mother and sisters fed them and tended their wounded. For this Christian charity they repaid us by pillaging and plundering our stores! That hidden cache of weapons they found gave them the excuse they wanted - to avenge this Royalist family. I curse them all.

'You are my son and heir and we must assess our situation and decide what can be done to appeal against such a sentence.' I stood helpless, looking at my poor father having to swallow this bitter pill, forced on him by such unlucky circumstances.

I knew that like many other Royalists, he had been forced to take the National Covenant and the Negative Oath to swear he would never take up arms against Parliament. Now he would have to find the money or have our estates sequestered.

Worse was to come. 'Unhappily, I have other debts,' my father admitted after a pause. 'They come to nearly £600 and I am obliged to pay £20 per annum to Mr Singleton of Gloucester from whom I have lately been forced to borrow money. Then there is £20 a year that must be paid to my brother Anthony.'

This I knew was an obligation to his only remaining younger brother entered into his marriage settlement, one that our grandfather had made him swear to meet.

My father riffled through some documents. 'Here it is,' he said, 'the sum total of the value of our estate, before these Troubles began. It comes to a paltry £274-8s, per annum.' He handed it to me and I read the list: £40 for the Manor of Clehonger, £126 for the Manors of Ford and Newton, £8 for the residence and lands in Hereford we called the Friars, and £100-8s for the land and tenements in Dorstone and Peterchurch.

'How can I find another £500 when I need money to pay for the repairs they all need? I curse the Scots – and the armies of both sides for the havoc they have wreaked!' He banged the desk top. 'I shall go to London and appeal personally against this injustice!'

I could only agree with his decision, although I thought such an undertaking would be expensive and perhaps to little avail. We had heard stories of wives and widows of seamen and soldiers trudging to the capital laden with their grievances and seeking relief. Even a petition presented by some thousands of maimed and wounded soldiers protesting their hardship, fell on unsympathetic ears.

Nevertheless, my father decided to submit himself to a Roundhead Committee in London, where an appeal for leniency of a man of his standing might more readily result in a reduction of his fine. His demeanour brightened once he had decided on this course of action, but on his return after weeks of anxious waiting, I could see at once that his journey had been in vain.

He told me what he said to the Committeemen, words that I shall remember to my dying day.

'Gentlemen,' he said, 'my place has been overrun by both armies. Over and above the distractions of my afrighted family, I have been rendered unable to put bread or drink into the mouths of my wife and seven children, but I was forced to go the fountain for one, and rely on the charity of strangers for the other.

I have seen my dwelling house destroyed by the King's army, which could not be repaired for less then £5,000 not counting what was lost by plunder and £570 of compulsory contributions.

I estimate the damage done by the Scots and the Parliamentary armies with plunder, contributions, free quarter to their troops, at £1,100. Greyfriars, demolished by the Royalists I valued at £2,000 and the materials taken from it to fortify Hereford Castle, I calculate at £300. My losses total £6,670.

May I remind you, with respect, of the suffering of my family, that their birth and breeding might have promised them better conditions.'

He told me the Committeemen listened politely enough to his appeal, put with such passion, but the sentence was upheld and they gave him two years to pay the fine.

He still had not straightened out my grandfather's affairs to the satisfaction of Richard Bevan, his tenant in Dorstone, for the man took out a case against my father at the Hereford Assizes demanding the return of the £10 that he was owed. Unfortunately, it happened the very time my father was in London appealing against his Delinquency, so he could not appeal in person and the case went against him.

Many of our kin, such as Colonel William Rudhall and Sir Walter Pye and of course Sir Henry Lingen, had also been similarly punished for their part in fighting for our anointed sovereign, God rest his soul. Some of the sentences meted out by the local Committeemen seemed grossly unfair and caused a deal of resentment in the county. Great-Uncle William had taken an active part in the war, having been commissioner for levying and training troops in the county for the Royalist army and being responsible for raising supplies. In July 1649, he was fined one sixth of the value of his property, or only £120, this being a fortunate consequence of his brother's will.

My father was particularly enraged that his cousin, Sir Walter Pye of the Mynde, who was in arms for the King, had his fine reduced on his appeal. Because he was in arms for the King and in Oxford when it surrendered, the Committee fined him £2,360, being one tenth the value of his property. Four years later, his fine was reduced to £333-6s-0d. He found the money to pay it immediately and his estates were discharged.

Parliament levied the huge sum of £6,342 on Sir Henry Lingen. Although raised as a Protestant by Lord Scudamore, he had a Catholic father, but more damning for him was the fact that he had been the most persistent Royalist commander in the county. After his defeat at Goodrich Castle, he and others in the garrison had been imprisoned in Hereford but liberated after two months and a promise never again to take up arms against Parliament.

In spite of that, not long after his release – and that of my Uncle Anthony - Sir Henry tried to foment a Royalist uprising. The plot was discovered and as a result, he was obliged to sell many of his estates for less than their true value, much to the despair of his wife and his heirs. In spite of his failings, Sir Henry Lingen still remains to me the beau ideal of a Cavalier – notwithstanding his later antagonism and treatment of Cousin Herbert Westfaling.

All the while, Colonel John Birch was enriching himself, spending his ill-gotten gains on the estates of those who were anxious to sell whatever land they could, at any price, to pay their fines, even to feed their children. Prices of land fell sharply. It infuriated my father to learn that Colonel Birch had bought Shelwyck Manor, which had been left to Sir Samuel in old Morgan Aubrey's will. My grandfather had been forced to sell it, being in straightened circumstances at the time.

I was almost nineteen years old when an event took place which had a profound effect on all of us. I refer of course to the execution of his anointed Majesty, King Charles I. None of us could believe that such a heinous crime and mortal sin could even be contemplated, much less committed. Our family and thousands of others went into mourning on learning that the dreadful act had indeed been carried out.

The smiling look His Majesty had bestowed on me only four years before, when he had graced us with his presence in Hereford, gave me strength and inspiration. We all prayed for his soul and I vowed again that I would devote my life to the service of the Monarch. With God's help, Prince Charles had escaped the wrath of the Parliamentarians and we knew he was waiting in Paris for a call to return to these shores as our rightful Sovereign.

In spite of his deprivations, my father had insisted that I return to the Hereford School. The school had changed little and I remember well, my school fellows and I forgetting our Latin and lapsing quickly into English as we compared experiences during the siege by the Scots. They had even taken part in the second line of defence, inspired as they were by the Governor, Colonel Barnabas Scudamore, a exciting feat that stirred envy in my heart. Colonel John Birch now governed Hereford in the name of Parliament, a once proud city, filth and beggars now sullied the streets. Daily we prayed for the return of our Monarch, for the world to be put to rights.

I did not leave the Hereford School with scholarly distinction, but my father was determined that I attend one of the Oxford colleges and then continue my studies at one of the Inns of Court. He believed that I acquire some knowledge of the law, knowing it to be an essential conclusion to my university studies and a preparation for the duty of overseeing his estates - what was left of them after the Committee for Compounding had done its worst. He himself had attended Magdalen College, but I set my heart on going to the Queen's College in Oxford, where I was more likely to meet young men with like theological leanings to mine.

I am happy to say that I succeeded in doing both; the first, thanks to my dear father, who struggled to find nearly £30 a year for my living costs at Oxford and the second, if I may say so without boasting, because of my own earnest endeavours. I soon discovered other youths with like-minded Royalist beliefs and we formed ourselves into an exclusive band. We were more than just 'Queen's Men', we called ourselves 'Archers', after the name for 'Bishop' in the game of chess which we played regularly. The association survived long after we bade farewell to those hallowed halls.

One fellow Archer whose esteem I never failed to honour, was that of Joseph Williamson[1], statesman and diplomatist-to-be. He too treasured the friendship we forged together at Oxford. He played an important part in my career.

The year I matriculated at that illustrious institution, Great-Uncle William Rudhall, the much respected old Cavalier went to his Maker, unmarried but greatly loved by all who knew him. I am not much given to romantic notions, but this story, which circulated widely at the time of his death, illustrates a degree of Christian charity in the county of Hereford, that sadly is not often found today.

As children, we had often heard our parents refer to 'that foreign wench' in the same breath as our great-uncle, and Anne had noticed that such references were always accompanied by an 'ahem' and an exchange of knowing looks. Now the old Cavalier was dead, the last male Rudhall of that line, one that had begun with so much promise.

I could not help but ponder on the possible wording of Great-Uncle William's will and those Rudhall properties that would come to my father, and in the fullness of time, to me.

Our family made the journey to Ross to pay their last respects to him at the parish church of St Mary the Virgin where so many Rudhalls were buried. The usual gaunt-looking 'sin-eater' from Ross performed the ancient ritual. Great-Uncle William's many nephews and nieces and their families, bonded in grief and many tenants from the estates crowded into the church with suitably down-cast faces. Seated beside Great-Aunt Mary and comforting her, was a woman of nondescript appearance. Only a large lace collar relieved her dark apparel and sombre looks.

Our parents made her acquaintance at last and Anne, as usual, discovered her history. Marie Suron, for that was her name, came from Provence. Being Huguonots, her father Jaques and his family suffered great persecution on the orders of Cardinal Richelieu so they fled the country and took refuge in England. They eventually settled in Ross and opened up a small shop. This way, Mademoiselle Marie, their only daughter, came to know members of our Grandmother Rudhall's family who would often shop there to buy their laces and ribbons.

Great-Uncle William befriended the young French girl and persuaded her to visit Rudhall Manor. Her visits became more frequent and according to Anne, gossip had it that marriage was in the air. She was very much younger than he, which would not have mattered, but she was foreign and what was worse, the daughter of a shop-keeper and one who could give her little in the way of a dowry, so of course marriage was out of the question.

Then came the Troubles and Great-Uncle William persuaded Marie and her parents to pack their belongings and stay at Rudhall Manor where they would be reasonably safe. They reluctantly agreed, and the Surons became a permanent fixture at the house, keeping Great-Aunt Mary company and in safe hands while he was away.

Soon after we lost the war, both Jacques Suron and his wife died. Great-Aunt Mary did all she could to comfort Marie in her grief. She could remain at Rudhall Manor and be her companion. But the French girl insisted on returning to Ross and starting a life of her own there.

After a time, she unexpectedly came into a great sum of money. Her friends suggested that she return to France, but it was too late for her to start again in what was now for her, a foreign country. Neither would she relinquish her belief in a Reformed Church and face possible persecution in her native land. She would stay in Ross where she had made many friends and would use her newly acquired wealth to help the poor.

Some time after Great-Uncle William's death, we heard the end of the story. Marie Suron ordered a marble statue be made of him wearing Roman military dress and arranged it to be placed by the plaques of his ancestors at the end of the south aisle of the parish church.

The inscription under the statue read:

To the ashes of William Rudhall, of Rudhall, Esquire, the last heir of the very illustrious and not less ancient family of Rudhall which he adorned, Mary Suron, spinster, erected this monument in token of her duty and affection. He died the 21st of September, in the year of Christ 1651.

The day the statue was completed, she went into the church and when she saw his likeness, she collapsed into sobs. On the best authority, and Anne confirmed the information, Marie Suron soon afterwards died of a broken heart, an affliction I believe, given to some women of an overly emotional disposition.

1. Sir Joseph Williamson (1633-1701), M.P. and Secretary of State. He worked his way up in the office of the Secretary of State, first as keeper of the King's Library, to Principal Secretary, then to the office itself.

He was briefly suspected of being involved in popish plotting and imprisoned in the Tower, but was released on the King's orders.

Sir Joseph was the second President of the Royal Society and was succeeded in that position by Sir Christopher Wren.

In his will, he left the school at Thetford £2,000 and £3,000 for the setting up of a 'Mathematical School' in Rochester, an institution still in existence.

18. Puritan London

Such a romantic story brings me back to my own life, for I felt obliged to delay thoughts of marriage while the country was in the hands of Oliver Cromwell and his henchmen.

I left the Queen's College Oxford even more committed to the beliefs of my forebears. All matters of Church and Monarchy for which my father, grandfather and uncle, and so many of my kin, had fought in vain for, were plainly the will of God - not that of the sanctimonious Puritans which we were then enduring. We knew in our hearts that it was only a matter of time before Cromwell would be ousted and our true monarch, King Charles II (as he had already been crowned in Scotland) would return in triumph to these shores and re-establish the Monarchy in all its traditional glory.

My old companion and close kin, Herbert Westfaling and I were admitted to Gray's Inn on the same day. Herbert and I were then, and remained for the rest of our lives, great friends. Herbert was tall like all the Rudhalls but wore a permanently perplexed expression as if concerned at what the future held for us – as indeed we all were. Both our paternal grandmothers were the daughters of William Rudhall and his wife Margaret Croft, and we often reflected on the political history of our mutual ancestors, but one family of particular interest to me, was that of the Crofts.

Sir William Croft, my father's cousin, had been one of the prisoners taken with my grandfather when Sir William Waller and his Parliamentarians captured Hereford in 1643. Two years later, Sir William Coft was slain, fighting for his King, at Stoke Say Castle in Shropshire. The whole family remained a shining example to all of us in those dreadful times when regicides ruled the land.

An earlier Croft, by the name of Richard, captured the son of Henry VI at Tewkesbury and handed him over with or without promise of the Prince's life, for £100. Then, after fighting for Henry VII when his reign was challenged, he was made a Knight Banneret and elevated to Treasurer, Keeper of the Wardrobe and Privy Councillor.

Another of that line, Sir James Croft was Lord Deputy of Ireland under Edward VI. When Catholic Mary came to the throne, he was unjustly implicated in Wyatt's rebellion, when people rose up in protest against her, and was remanded for a time to the Tower. While in prison he often saw his fellow-prisoner the Lady Elizabeth as she was then known. She was confined there while her enemies searched in vain for evidence to implicate her in the plot against her half-sister Queen Mary.

When Elizabeth came to the throne, the new Queen granted Sir James much land in Herefordshire and Kent and appointed him Seneschal of Hereford, a cathedral administrator. She also made him Controller of the Queen's Household and a Privy Councillor. He acquired still more land and represented Herefordshire in the Parliament for many years.

The deeds of the Crofts never ceased to inspire me – and my Cousin Herbert - illustrating as they did, how loyalty and devotion to one's King would surely be richly rewarded. We knew that people of power have always opened doors of opportunity for lesser mortals, men who served them with devotion - and with rectitude. I vowed that I too, would always serve my King no matter what the circumstances - and we both agreed that at some future date, we would represent the city of Hereford in Whitehall.

Herbert committed himself relentlessly to that youthful goal. My success came much later than his. I had many trials to test my resolve but my loyalty to His Majesty never wavered. It pleased me to hear of discontent against the Roundheads surfacing into scattered uprisings throughout the country and rumours of plans to welcome the return of King Charles II brought joy to my heart. But before this happy event took place, for which we prayed daily, my father and mother were to suffer still more sorrow.

My young sister Judith became ill with the fever to which my mother attributed the deprivation and hardship she had been forced to endure at a crucial age in her childhood. Our servant Marie Dating, an old, motherly woman who had lived with us for years, hardly left her side and the surgeon came and bled her daily. When she could, my mother urged Judith to drink a potion of herbs that she had made with her own hands, but the girl did not respond and expired after a matter of days. Her death brought my two sisters Anne and Mary closer together while my other sister Elizabeth and my mother remained inseparable.

No sooner had Judith gone to her Maker, than Godwin left these shores having signed on with George Swanley, a mariner and landowner from Essex who traded in foreign parts.

Even as a small boy, my brother never feared danger. He was lean and strong, and when he incurred my wrath I have to admit he could best me with his fists or escape from me so fast I could never catch him. Above all he loved the water. We usually explained Godwin's long absences to his having gone down to the River Wye to fish or to swim. So it did not surprise me to learn that he had persisted in going to sea and was now satisfying his love of adventure by sailing to ports in the Ottoman Empire.

Young Thomas, indolent as always, was still bemoaning his fate at being a younger son, and struggling with his studies while casting his eyes longingly towards London.

Encouraged by my mother, who was instrumental in arranging the union, my father negotiated the marriage settlement of my sister Anne to William Boothby, a member of her Merchant Taylor family. He felt that since the Troubles had abated, he now had the means to provide a dower for her in keeping with her status as the daughter of Herbert Aubrey of Clehonger.

Anne and my other two sisters all agreed that it was high time she married and that the young man was personable and well established and would make an eminently suitable husband. It was as well the two young people liked each other, because I knew that Anne would require a strong man to control her. Her curiosity was as insatiable as ever, but I was pleased to observe that she had at last learned to curb some of her unladylike behaviour and demeanour. My sisters were almost as excited as Anne at the prospect of a family wedding in London, especially one that brought together the Aubreys and the Boothbys. They could talk of little else.

The wedding took place on the nineteenth day of May in the year of Our Lord 1657 at the old St Pancras Church in Soper Lane, a wealthy parish that included prosperous shopkeepers on Cheapside and rich merchants involved in the colonial trade. We all gathered there for the occasion, which allowed me to meet some of our distant kinsmen from my mother's Boothby family, many of whom were men of real substance.

None of them had suffered during the recent Troubles as we had in Herefordshire, and not all of them saw eye to eye with me on matters of faith and Christian principles. One of the gathering, a Merchant Taylor with a complacent and self-satisfied air, even had the temerity to tell me to my face that he admired the deeds of Cromwell, who had by now been given the title of Lord Protector. I retorted that he certainly would need the Lord to protect him. The man, obviously a Puritan, just smiled and I could see that nothing would lift the veil from such ignorant eyes.

My stay in London gave me the opportunity of meeting my young Cousin Ralph Hawtrey. Although he and I were of an age, he rather towered over me in height, but we soon found much in common. His mother Mary Bedell, my mother's sister, had been married to Ralph Hawtrey, Citizen of London and Merchant Taylor, a man with whom their father Mathew Bedell had financial connections.

My father resented the fact that old Mathew Bedell, noted for his wealth and piety, had ignored him in a bizarre aspect of his will. In it, my grandfather Bedell directed that his house and land in West Purley, near Croydon, were to be sold at his death and all the specified legacies, paid

---

Mathew Bedell of London, Citizen, Alderman & Merchant Taylor (d.c1636)
= 1) (c1597) Margaret, dau Simon Lawrence, widow of Titus Westby

  |

   1. Ann = (14 Apr 1620) Thomas Mustard, Citizen & Grocer (d.c1636)
   2. Prudence = Thomas Thorald, Citizen & Ironmonger (d.c1651)
   3. Mathew Bedell (d.c1598)
   4. Martha = (1636) Richard Taverner

= 2) (9Jul1608) Anne dau William Boothby of London, Citizen &
                                                    Merchant Taylor

  |

   5. Benjamin Bedell (b.1609)
   6. Elizabeth (1609-1676) = (8 Jul 1628) Herbert Aubrey of Clehonger
   7. Mary (1610-1655)
      = 1) (1630) Ralph Hawtrey (1602-1645) Citizen & Merchant Taylor of
                                                    Ruislip, Middlesex
      = 2) (1649) Lewis Audley, Parliamentarian
   8. Thomas Bedell (b.1616)

= 3) (10 Mar 1635) Elizabeth Bird at St Gregory by St Pail

---

out of the proceeds. However, if either one of his sons-in-law, Thomas Thorold or Ralph Hawtrey, the husbands of his daughters Prudence and Mary respectively, would pay the legacies, they should take the land. His other son-in-law, Thomas Mustard had died by this time, but he offered my father, very much alive in Herefordshire, no part at all in this odd arrangement.

Even as a small child, I can remember my parents having endless discussions about Grandfather Bedell's will. I understood nothing of my father's harsh words and his resentment at being excluded from his father-in-law's offer. But I was not to know that I too, would be a victim of this unfair testament.

Ralph Hawtrey's family had occupied the Chequers Estate set among the Chiltern Hills in Buckinghamshire for more than three hundred years and for over a century, they had prospered, largely by capturing a monopoly of Anglo-Russian trade. Aunt Mary's husband Mr Hawtrey

---

Ralph Hawtrey of Ruislip (1570-1638) = Mary Altham, dau Edward Altham Esq
of Mark Hall, Latton, co Essex

1. John Hawtrey (1600-1658) = Susanna James
2. Edward Hawtrey, Vicar of Burnham (1600-1669) =
Margaret Wright, widow
3. Ralph Hawtrey (1602-1645) = Mary Bedell (1610-1655)

1. Ralph Hawtrey (1631-1713) 'soldier & adventurer'
of Westmeath & Tiperary
2. Matthew Hawtrey (b.1632)
3. Mary (b.1634)
4. Thomas Hawtrey (b.1635)
5. Anne (b.1636) = Mainwaring
6. Gertrude (1637-1638)
7. Mary (b.1639) = Blackwell of Mortlake, Surrey
8. Elizabeth (b.1641-) = George Sitwell
9. John Hawtrey (1642-1678) Vicar of Sanderstead, Surrey
10. Martha (d.1718) = George Booth

4. Mary (c1604-1661) = Sir John Bankes of Corfe Castle

---

was easily able to pay the legacies and so acquired Mathew Bedell's land and had grown fat on it.

Then for some unaccountable reason, after Mr Hawtrey died, my mother's sister took for her second husband, the Parliamentarian, Lewis Audley, who now enjoyed his position as master of the Widow Hawtrey's property.

What Lady Bankes, Mr Hawtrey's sister thought of the union, I could not imagine. I well remember my dear mother telling us the story of how Aunt Mary's sister-in-law distinguished herself by defending Corfe Castle against the Parliamentarians. At one stage, facing an assault and aided only by five soldiers and with the help of her daughters, she held out against the rebels by hurling stones and hot embers down onto the rebels below, so foiling their attempt assail the castle.

Lady Bankes held out for three terrible years before she was forced to capitulate as a result of a treacherous action by a member of her garrison. In defeat, her possessions were plundered and the castle was reduced to rubble. The first time I heard the story, I considered it to be a most wonderful sacrifice in the Royalist cause and an amazing feat for one of the fair sex. Naturally, Aunt Mary's marriage to the Parliamentarian Lewis Audley severed the connection between the two women completely.

However, all differences were put aside in the celebration of Anne's nuptials, and William Boothby's family and our many Merchant Taylor cousins showed us great consideration, in spite of their Puritan leanings. After the wedding, and making the acquaintance of our Boothby cousins, my sister Mary begged permission to delay her return to Clehonger and remained in the Capital under the protection of her now married sister to whom she had grown close over the years.

Every letter Mary sent home to Clehonger was full of enthusiasm, in spite of the restrictions to people's daily lives brought in by the Puritans, constraints about which more and more people complained. London's theatres were shut down and Sunday sports were banned. Soldiers were empowered to enter houses to ensure their inhabitants were observing the Sabbath, and anyone found vainly walking on the Lord's Day was penalised.

The strict rules enforcing godliness and public worship were ones with which I could only agree, but I could not condone the banning of the celebration of Christmas. I could never believe that commemorating with joy Our Lord's birthday amounted merely to a Papist superstition, as the Puritans claimed.

Nevertheless, nothing diminished Mary's enjoyment of London. I remember she even amazed my mother when she wrote that she had sampled the new drinking chocolate, that was now the rage.

Suddenly her letters stopped. For days, my mother waited for the post from London but in vain. Then to our dismay, we learnt that Mary had died, suddenly and without warning, leaving my parents in the midst of all their other worries, to bear the loss of yet another of their children; this one on the threshold of so much life and promise.

My mother supported my father with her usual fortitude as he grieved for the daughter who, from the time she was a little girl, had always managed to bring a smile to his face. We all felt the loss of one to whom our parents were devoted and whose laughter we would never again hear. He was given the sad task of administering her will while for my part, matters of finance continued to test my faith in human nature.

19. Restoration

My friendship with my Cousin Ralph Hawtrey, blossomed as we became more firmly united in our dislike of his step-father. A tall, gangling lad with piercing eyes, young Ralph often came to stay with us at Clehonger, being especially fond of his aunt, my mother.

'How my sainted Mama could have agreed to marry that Parliamentarian, I'll never fathom! He is avaricious and parsimonious, concerned only with enriching himself at the expense of Royalists!' he would complain to me in private. I could only agree. It stuck in my craw to think that my poor father, the old Cavalier, had spared no effort to pay his fine, repair the damage done to his property and discharge my grandfather's debts. We nursed these grievances well into the night.

During the course of the war, Mr Lewis Audley had taken every opportunity to increase his land holding, buying up sequestered estates from Royalists desperate for money. He bought Sir John Hatton's estate in Long Stanton and Oakington in Cambridgeshire and Thoresway Manor in Lincolnshire, part of the sequestered estate of Sir John Culpepper, formerly Master of the Rolls and a leading supporter of His Late Majesty. When he satisfied his acquisitiveness further by buying Sir Robert Hatton's estate in Hogginton in Cambridgeshire, he promptly demanded higher rents from the tenants and was deaf to their pleas for relief from this additional burden. I knew that many more who had served the King were still struggling even to survive.

As a major in the Parliamentary army, Aunt Mary's new husband was notorious for his assault on the North Downs near Surbiton in Surrey in 1648. The Royalists, led by Henry Rich the Earl of Holland, had been forced to retreat to Kingston and in the resulting battle Lord Francis Villiers, younger brother of the Duke of Buckingham, had his horse killed under him. By using an elm to guard his back, he bravely kept several Roundheads at bay until one of them crept up behind him, knocked off his steel cap and struck him on the head. When news of this reached London, orders came that Lord Villiers was to be treated with care. Major Audley casually announced his death and added 'and good pillage was found in his pocket.'

Ralph and I were close then, but our friendship came to an abrupt end when I heard that he sold the estate he had inherited at West Purley to his step-father. In fact, I considered this deed tantamount to treachery, considering the man's history and his part during and after the Troubles. Ralph endeavoured to convince me of his own great financial need at the time, how he wanted the money to seek his fortune abroad and how Lewis Audley was at heart sympathetic to our Church, but I refused to listen to his feeble excuses.

This action was connected to the other grave injustice, heaped upon myself and my mother, that stemmed from Grandfather Bedell's will. The old man had stated that the sale of his lands in Surrey were to provide legacies for his daughters, one of them being my mother, and their children. The youngest sons would each receive £50, but not the eldest because he would inherit his father's estate.

My mother's eldest son was of course Samuel and he was still alive back in 1636 when Mathew Bedell wrote his will. I should have been listed as a younger son as indeed I was at the time. But because after Samuel's death, I became my father's heir, a confusion arose and as a result, I failed to receive my rightful share of my grandfather's inheritance.

Ralph Hawtrey, Aunt Mary's first husband, who acquired Mathew Bedell's land according to the agreement, and whose duty it was to pay the legacies as a result, was now dead. Nevertheless, they all knew the true circumstances of my birth and the death of my older brother Samuel and against my dear mother's wishes, I took Mr Audley and young Ralph Hawtrey whom I held responsible for this omission, to the Court of Chancery.

I accused my cousin and his step-father of plotting together to deprive me of the monies that should have come to me from my grandfather's will. In all modesty, I believe that I impressed the defendants with my knowledge of the law when I demanded that they tell the Court under what conditions the properties in the will were conveyed to them and why my grandfather's legacy of £50 had not been granted to me.

Mr Audley's Council rose to his feet and with an unctuous smile bowed and said,

'My Lord, we admit nothing. Mr Aubrey here does not meet the criteria as set out so explicitly in the will of the late lamented Mr

Bedell. Why? Because his name is not Samuel! Neither has the money has been paid to anyone else, and even if my esteemed client were obliged to pay £50 to a Mr *Samuel* Aubrey now, he would no longer be in a position to do so.' He sat down with what I can only describe as a look of triumph.

The case dragged on and was finally dismissed, and so fate singled me out to bear this singular injustice of being deprived of the £50 that by rights, should have been mine. I consoled myself as best I could with the fact that as soon as Great-Aunt Mary Rudhall died, I personally would perhaps inherit something from her estate.

The King had graciously issued his Declaration of Breda which promised indemnity for all except those that Parliament should exclude, as well as, among other matters, a land settlement, the whole to be subject to the approval of a new Parliament. Such a magnanimous Monarch as he boded well for the future of England, especially for those of us who owned land - so happy and relieved was I and all our kin. Once again we would see true Royalists at Westminster representing the counties of England.

Cousin Herbert was fortunate enough to find himself in London the day of His Majesty's arrival. He was thus able to witness personally, the magnificent return of our King to these shores. I had chosen to sacrifice the journey there in order to collect the rent due from one of our recalcitrant tenants, as my brother Thomas, who usually took on this task, had betaken himself to the Capital to find employment there. Thus I was forced to hear details of the occasion second hand, from Herbert's lips when he returned to Hereford soon afterwards.

'As he crossed the London Bridge, the bells peeled and trumpets sounded. The crowd roared so much, you could hardly hear yourself speak. First the hundreds of troops of gentlemen, some in scarlet gowns, others in purple, flashes of green and lilac, the Lord Mayor and Aldermen in their scarlet robes, shining white and brilliant yellow wherever one looked. And His Majesty! Adorned in silver and gold lace! Shone like the sun itself, seated between his two younger brothers, the Dukes of York and Gloucester, all in magnificent procession to the Palace of Whitehall...'

I had needs interrupt Herbert's interminable narrative, to remind him that we too in Hereford celebrated in like fashion, but with no less ardour than that expressed by the people of London. Our church bells peeled in exultation the whole day long, and there was great celebration of feasting and drinking of ale and dancing round the maypole. I said a special and private prayer, thanking God for His Majesty's safe return and asked Him to bless his long and happy reign.

Events moved swiftly after the rejoicing and at first, all seemed promising, as every shire and county sent representatives to the Convention Parliament held to vote and make official, the restoration of the Monarchy. Nothing pleased me more when the Freemen of Hereford elected my dear Cousin Herbert, together with Roger Bosworth, a physician and my father's friend, to the Convention Parliament.

The first upset came when Dr Bosworth died and in his place the voters elected the old Cavalier Sir Henry Lingen, my Uncle Anthony's former Colonel-in-Chief. The wounds he had sustained in battle and the worry of finding the money to pay his huge delinquency fine had taken their toll. Among his long black curls, I noticed strands of grey, but his dark eyes still held their piercing and commanding gaze. I considered him an exemplary Royalist who had paid dearly for his steadfast loyalty to the King but my admiration was often tempered by his frequent lack of decorum and his exhibitionist behaviour.

Next we prepared for the General Election for the first official Parliament of King Charles' reign. Every county was to elect two Knights of the Shire and two Burgesses for the City. The question of who would represent the county of Hereford was on everyone's lips, while Herbert busied himself tirelessly, making himself agreeable to as many Freemen of the City as he could.

I let it be known that I would be proud to serve my country in such a capacity, but it soon became obvious that I did not have the necessary support. Being an open borough with a wide franchise, Hereford elections were notoriously expensive and I consoled myself with the melancholy fact that my financial affairs were becoming such a burden that I had needs bide my time.

Naturally, Herbert intended to stand for election as one of the two Burgesses in the new Parliament, but the cost of such an undertaking had been more than he had anticipated and he confessed that he had been forced to borrow heavily against his future Rudhall inheritance.

Those of us who lead righteous lives are ever the target for the deluded and the headstrong and it pains me now to look back on that sorry episode, the first general election for Members of Parliament after the return of our rightful Monarch, an occurrence that almost destroyed Cousin Herbert Westfaling's hopes and expectations.

He naturally believed the voters had the same confidence in him as before, when they elected him to the Convention Parliament, having knowledge of his care and fidelity. But to his distress, malicious rumours began circulating. Stories spread that that far from being Royalist, his family had actively supported the Commonwealth. Of course everyone knew, save those with short memories and wayward beliefs, that he and his family had always expressed the deepest of Royalist sympathies.

Herbert's father had died of the smallpox before the Troubles and therefore played no part in them and his grandfather, the Bishop's son who married Frances Rudhall, my grandmother's older sister, had completely wasted away her fortune in pursuing his wasteful and fruitless enterprises that we as children used to ponder over. As a result, being forced to sell most of his property, he died £800 in debt, leaving his executors to pay his creditors an amount that came to nearly one year's income. Dear old Great-Aunt Mary Rudhall never forgave the suffering his actions had caused her sister.

These malicious tales, implying that Cousin Herbert had misled the voters of Hereford as to his allegiance to the Crown, spread throughout the county and I traced their source to Sir Henry Lingen. To my dismay, Sir Henry sought to oust Herbert and to have in his place his old friend and fellow Cavalier, Sir Edward Hopton of Stoke Edith.

I knew that Sir Edward had fought gallantly at the storming of Leicester and had been personally knighted by His Late Majesty Charles I, God rest his soul. In spite of that honour, his own father had favoured Parliament during the Troubles, and two of his brothers had even fought on their side. I could not bear to see such a man, bred from a family with such divided loyalties, take the place of my dear cousin.

The two knights and their agents began to oppose Herbert in every way, using persecution, threats and intimidation against those who were for him. Contrary to his obligations, the Mayor refused to make a Freeman of the City any voter who supported Mr Westfaling, only those who promised to give their votes for the knights.

The day of the election dawned and I joined my cousin at the Guildhall, where divers young men, being formerly denied their freedom by the Mayor unless they promised to give their votes for the knights, had gathered together. The mood grew ugly and some had even drawn their swords.

Nothing would satisfy them but to hold the Mayor there, demanding their freedom from him and thus their eligibility to vote – for Herbert. They claimed that a number of Sir Edward's 251 so-called voters were doubly set down, some almsmen, and some were even minors. Of course the Mayor vehemently denied any errors and certainly any wrong-doing.

In the meantime, Sir Henry Lingen and Sir Edward Hopton and their supporters were waiting in the Shire Hall for the Mayor to come and declare the poll, so confident were they of success. When they learnt that Herbert's supporters were holding His Worship at the Guildhall, the two knights commanded the trumpets to sound to horse. The soldiers, part of their entourage, quickly mounted. The two old Cavaliers drew their swords and they and their supporters charged at full gallop to the Guildhall in such a violent manner that they knocked over men, women and children and many bystanders on their way. Mayhem ensued.

One of Herbert's supporters spied the knights and their men galloping towards the Guildhall and shouted for the door to be shut and barred. Herbert and I drew our swords, fearing for our lives. Fortunately, a number of other country gentry were present to witness the ugly scene. Amid the uproar, Sir John Scudamore, the Sheriff, shouted for the door of the Guildhall be opened.

I remember Sir Edward Harley – the former Parliamentarian and now Royalist - endeavoured to pacify the uproar, but to little avail. Sir William Powell, a tall man with a commanding presence, ordered the soldiery to retreat forthwith. Had we not been present, there would have been blood spilt.

When the turmoil subsided, the Sheriff instructed the three contestants and their agents adjourn to the house of Mr Wellington, the apothecary.

Once there, the Mayor insisted on declaring for the knights but Herbert demanded a poll against Sir Edward Hopton but allowed Sir Henry Lingen. Then they disputed how they should conduct the poll. The knights insisted upon polling together, and that each Freeman should declare for two persons. Herbert swore he would stand only with Sir Edward Hopton. Tempers remained on a knife-edge although Herbert managed to keep his dignity through all the shouting and tumult. At last the Freemen agreed to meet the next day at the Shire Hall, without any manner of weapons, offensive or defensive.

Word swept through the city that Sir Edward Hopton had prevailed upon the Mayor to stay that night with him, and sure enough, the next day that worthy dignitary addressed the assembled crowd from the window of Sir Edward's lodging. The Mayor declared the result to the growing crowd below. The two knights should sit in the next Parliament as Burgesses for the City of Hereford, and bade Mr Westfaling accept the decision.

At that, the Freemen below waved their fists and shouted their disapproval. Herbert and I, his friends and supporters made our way to the Shire Hall. There they subscribed their names in a written list, which amounted to at least two hundred and fifty in number. Then there were indentures made, signed by several Aldermen and Common Council and delivered to the Sheriff.

The count was again taken: Herbert was returned first, and Sir Henry Lingen second. At that declaration of the poll, cheers and hurrahs rent the air and Herbert was carried about the High Cross in a chair, attended by the gentlemen and most of the Freemen of the City. The townspeople, men women and children, followed him crying, 'Westfaling! Westfaling!'.

Glad as I was for Herbert, I knew that he had spent £1,200 on the contest, an amount he could ill afford, even though he stood to inherit much of the Rudhall property when Great-Aunt Mary died.

The whole sorry business saddened my father who held Sir Henry Lingen in such high regard as one of the most valiant defenders of the Royalist cause, under whom his brother Anthony had served so loyally.

Now fate intervened, for in the following winter of January 1662, on the way home from London, Sir Henry Lingen fell ill of the small pox at Gloucester and died, leaving his wife Alice in great financial hardship.

In his place, voters elected as a Member for Hereford young Roger Vaughan, a kinsman of mine, a protégé of Herbert, and described by all as 'a worthy and hopeful gentleman'. Only later did I see the irony in that epithet.

At the time, it pleased me greatly that I had two kinsmen in Westminster serving His Majesty: Herbert Westfaling and Roger Vaughan - the latter, a young man I trusted to my cost.

20. Kinship & Marriage

My father was already receiving some of the rents from old William Rudhall's estate, to which, in the fullness of time, would be mine to enjoy. In his will, Great-Uncle William had devised to Great-Aunt Mary, in trust, all those Rudhall estates that had eventually come to him, with the instruction to divide them into eighteen equal parts and allot them to the descendants of their sisters, one of whom was my father.

As a result of the partition of the estate, he inherited the manors of Brampton Abbots and Gatsford about two miles north of Ross, including Gatsford farm house and a meadow commonly called 'Great Rise', all in the parish of Brampton Abbots. The bequest came at an opportune time for the fortunes of our family.

Being descended from old William Rudhall's eldest daughter Frances, Cousin Herbert Westfaling received a larger portion than the others. He also stood to inherit Rudhall Manor after Great-Aunt Mary's death. Pleased for my dear father and his inheritance, I did not allow the twinge of envy to taint the friendship that had developed between Herbert and me over the years.

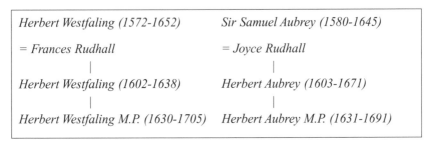

Herbert Westfaling (1572-1652)	Sir Samuel Aubrey (1580-1645)
= Frances Rudhall	= Joyce Rudhall
Herbert Westfaling (1602-1638)	Herbert Aubrey (1603-1671)
Herbert Westfaling M.P. (1630-1705)	Herbert Aubrey M.P. (1631-1691)

I and indeed all who knew him, held Herbert in high esteem for the uprightness of his character and those of his forebears. His great-grandfather's stone effigy in the Cathedral Church of Hereford, lying prone and praying, remained untouched by the Parliamentary hordes during the Troubles and was a constant reminder of that Bishop's bounty and goodness.

My father had borrowed money to enlarge his land holding to bring in more money in rents. It now included property in the parishes of

Wharton and Peterchurch and a small parcel of land at Eaton Bishop, close to Clehonger, but somehow, the cloud of financial deprivation still hung over us.

I knew we were not alone in bearing such a cross. Cousin Herbert was indebted to the scriveners in London as a result of his standing for Hereford, and many of our kin were still struggling from the effects of having to find money to pay their fines to Parliament, as well as paying interest on the sums they had been forced to borrow even to live.

Nevertheless, Herbert's countenance now wore less of a worried expression, for a few years earlier he had wed Anne, the daughter of Sir Thomas Edwards of Greet in Shropshire and was ever fond of extolling the virtues of having a wife and urging me to enter the married state.

With our rightful King on the throne and the joy we still felt, my father also considered that it was time for me to enter the honourable state of Holy Matrimony, encouraged as we all were by the marriage of His Majesty with Catherine, the daughter of King John of Portugal.

I had decided on one of the daughters of a gentleman of our acquaintance as a possible wife, but she failed to meet the high standards of feminine virtues I had set in my mind for the future partner in my life. And besides, being one of four girls, her father had but little property and

---

John Brydges of Priors Court Herefordshire = Joyce Bright (c1614-1669)
    |

1. Dorothy Brydges (c1636-1667) = Walter Thomas of Swansea

2. Joyce Brydges (1638-1712) = Herbert Aubrey II of Clehonger (1631-1691)
                    |

             Herbert Aubrey III (1664-1744)
             Joyce (1666-1716)
             Brydges Aubrey (1669-1691)
             Reginald Aubrey (1676-1742)
             Elizabeth (b.1679)

3. Margaret Brydges (c1640-1666) = Thomas Carpenter of Lincoln's Inn
                  |

             Theodosia Carpenter = (20 Jun 1677) Lemuel Kingdon of Whitehall
                                     (c1654-1686)

---

so would not have been able to do justice to her reputed beauty in the matter of her dowry.

Being cognisant of all this, Herbert made it possible on numerous occasions for me to be in the company of Joyce, the second daughter of John Brydges of Priors Court in Dormington. He considered Mr Brydges to be a worthy friend (of whom Herbert had many) and a man of infinite kindness. With such a recommendation, and after much thought on my part and encouragement on that of Herbert's, I decided that Joyce Brydges would be eminently suitable as the mother of my children.

The Brydges descended from an ancient and distinguished lineage, and the family had owned land and estates in Herefordshire for generations. This I must aver was a much more cogent reason for my choice of a wife than the fact that she and her two sisters were the sole heirs of their father's estate.

So I began wooing Miss Brydges. I found her to be a quiet and retiring young woman, petite and buxom, with all the necessary graces, and one whom I knew could be persuaded to accede readily to all my wishes. I started making frequent visits to Priors Court to pay my respects while my father found time to renew his association with Mr Brydges, a kindly man who always welcomed us warmly. As my acquaintance with him grew, it soon became apparent that he favoured me above her other suitors, of whom there were but few.

Her family included many men of consequence to recommend it to me, especially her many cousins and uncles. Her father had been Sheriff of Herefordshire as had her uncle William Brydges of Tibberton Court. Of more immediate interest to me was a cousin, of whom Joyce was particularly fond. The young lady had married Bridstock Harford, a man of my own age, a lawyer and the son of old Doctor Harford known to all the inhabitants of Hereford. Young Bridestock aspired to represent Hereford at Westminster, as did I, so in that respect we had much in common. I little dreamed that the Doctor would, in time, be linked to me by marriage.

Unhappily, both he and his son were known to be implacable enemies of the King - a blot on the family escutcheon that Joyce's father did not consider as shameful as I did. I vowed that after my marriage, I would do everything in my utmost to persuade young Bridstock and his father to see the error of their ways.

When I remember my own and my family's numerous ailments, I pride myself that I succeeded, because when old Doctor Harford later rebuilt the Hereford Hospital, he had inscribed over its portal: 'Fear God, honour the King, relieve the poor'. Such a sentiment gave all who read it, much solace and comfort, and me, much gratification.

Of lesser consequence were her siblings. Joyce's older sister Dorothy had wed Walter Thomas of Swansea and the younger sister Margaret had recently married Thomas Carpenter of Lincoln's Inn, a barrister-at-law. The only offspring of that union was a young hussey they named Theodosia.

At first Miss Brydges showed some reluctance to reciprocate my feelings for her, using a ploy often resorted to by young ladies, in order to 'stoke the flames of my ardour' as I remember putting it to her. My visits to Priors Court became more frequent as I succeeded in lessening the reservations I still noted in Joyce's manner towards me. But with her father's encouragement and my persistence in pursuit of her hand, she at last agreed to be mine.

Finally both our fathers agreed on the terms of the marriage contract and Mr Brydges paid us £1,650 as Joyce's portion to make me the happiest of men. The King of Portugal had paid £300,000 for his daughter's dowry, but I assured Joyce she should not feel uneasy on that score when she compared hers to Her Majesty's.

So we were united in Holy Matrimony in the old stone parish church of St Peter in Dormington where Joyce and her sisters had been baptised. With that enjoining of the Brydges and the Aubreys, and the help of my friends, especially that of my Fellow Archer from Oxford days, Joseph Williamson, my future seemed assured, debts or no. I wrote to him often, keeping him abreast of my own humble accomplishments.

Joyce, always solicitous of her parents' health, being their only close daughter, made me mindful of the fact that my dear father had aged considerably and his beard was now streaked with silver. It saddened me to see that worry over all these years had taken such a toll. Problems of money, or the lack thereof, continued to beset us and our woes came not in single file.

To his dismay, he was selected to hold the office of Sheriff. I remember our grandfather telling us – he had been made Sheriff in 1622 and most of our kin had held the position at some stage in their lives –

that one could never refuse such an offer. The duties were onerous and time-consuming and by law he was personally responsible for any mistakes or excesses made by the bailiffs or court officials in his name.

I immediately wrote to my old friend Joseph in London thus,

> *'I beg your interest, as an ancient Fellow Archer, in preventing my Father's being made Sheriff for Herefordshire or Suffolk for both of which he is liable. He is an old Cavalier, and has been a great sufferer and this employment will continue him so.'*

To our relief, Joseph used his friendships to good effect and my father did not have to bear that additional burden. It was just one of the many acts of kindness he bestowed on me over the years.

Even with the small Rudhall inheritance, my father was still struggling financially although Anne's dowry had been taken care of, Mary was dead and my sister Elizabeth had – foolishly I thought - spurned several offers of marriage. She expressed the shameful idea that she preferred to manage her own finances – the little my father would be able to leave her – rather than enter the married state and have all belong to her husband.

My father had more worries to concern him. After much importuning on the part of my grandfather's creditors, they took him to court, claiming that before Sir Samuel died, he had assured them that his son would pay the money they were owed out of rents from the Clehonger estate.

They even begrudged the fact that my father had managed to rescue Sir Samuel's horses and plate and other possessions from Greyfriars before it was demolished, and had kept it all for himself. They maintained my father should have used those chattels to pay some of the debts – never mind that he was at the time in such in dire financial straits. Nevertheless, my father was ordered to pay off Sir Samuel's creditors, together with the accrued interest.

No sooner had my grandfather's creditors been satisfied when my father had to bear the additional burden of paying a tax on the number of hearths in the house in which we lived. Twice a year we were obliged to pay two shillings per hearth. Our mansion house at Clehonger had more hearths than any other house in the parish - thirteen, which meant my father had to find an additional £2-12s-0 a year.

As for me, I was made a Commissioner for Assessment, which position I held for nearly twenty years. My duties included evaluating property or income for the purposes of taxation and they were amply suited to my inclination, my temperament and my talents.

I then considered it appropriate to enlarge my own landholding in addition to the property my wife had brought with her according to the terms of my marriage settlement. I rented six acres of arable land in Clehonger called Bowling Green Close from Hereford Cathedral for forty shillings down and an annual rent of three shillings a year, plus a field known as Oatehill, adjoining our estate. I had to borrow rather heavily in the process for that, as well as having to fulfil my obligations to pay the Hearth Tax and to find money for the new Militia Assessment.

This latter scheme was brought in by His Majesty's Government to provide a localised army whose loyalty to the Crown was unimpeachable. No more Cromwell's so-called New Model Army. Instead, owners of property worth over £50 a year were called upon to provide horses and foot-soldiers, arms, ammunitions, cartage and supplies. Choice of commanding officers were naturally a Royal prerogative, and I was honoured to learn that my kinsman Thomas Price had been chosen as one of them.

This fact helped to soften the blow when we learned that we now had to find a total of £412-13s-4d for our properties in Clehonger, Dorstone, Eaton Bishop, Peterchurch and Wharton as our contribution to the Militia. Even when our tenants brought their rents on the due dates, I was often forced to apply to the local scrivener for a loan. I instructed Joyce to make what economies she could, but for some reason she found that difficult and money was always short.

All these problems eventually faded into insignificance when Joyce was brought to bed with a son and heir, a boy for whom I thanked God and on whom I pinned such hopes. I named him, I thought appropriately, Herbert Aubrey; the third of that honourable name.

To ease my growing financial worries, my dear father bought all my messuages, lands tenements and hereditaments situated in the parish of Peterchurch, which gave me the opportunity to enlarge the manor at Clehonger. Unfortunately, the two new additional hearths I had put in place, meant paying an extra eight shillings per annum, but I considered the improvement to be a fitting reflection of my status in the county and thus well worth the added outlay.

My father intended to lease the farm at Peterchurch in order to be able to fulfil my great-grandfather Morgan Aubrey's wishes and pay the annual £4 annuity to the poor of Llanfrynach, where he grew up. My great-grandmother Joane Aubrey, who died after her husband Morgan, had directed in her will that my grandfather, Sir Samuel, honour her husband's wishes in this regard, but debts and war had resulted in an arrears of payments, and my dear father felt an obligation to rectify this.

My dear mother bore these financial hardships with her customary stoicism, an aspect of her character and wifely virtue that I was ever obliged to remind Joyce she should emulate.

Cousin Herbert had no such domestic concerns. While spending so much of his time in London, his wife had taken upon herself to care for Great-Aunt Mary Rudhall in the manor house that would one day be theirs.

To me, Westminster seemed ever more far away.

21. Testing Times

Throughout all these travails, I wrote regularly to Joseph Williamson, my friend and Fellow Archer, as I was always pleased to remind him, giving him snippets of valuable information concerning the allegiances of noteworthy individuals in the county, all this in the course of asking him if he could keep me in mind if any positions of a pecuniary nature should be in his pocket.

Even as a young man, Joseph's commanding presence and dark eyes under heavy brows instilled awe and respect, particularly among the younger scholars, and as I remember, his tutors as well. Many is the time I deemed it prudent to allow him to check mate me in the games of chess we all regularly played.

Joseph had left the hallowed halls of the Queen's College an elected Fellow and a Master of Arts. By now he had become very proficient with the viols he so loved to play to an admiring audience, and had entered political life - at a propitious time for both of us. He had obtained a place in the office of Sir Edward Nicholas, Secretary of State, another old Queen's man, and held the position of Keeper of the King's Library at Whitehall. He was moving in ever more influential spheres.

I always made a point of enquiring after him through my dear Cousin Herbert, now often away in London, and 'our eternally honoured friend' as I put it, Henry Ball, another Queen's man and Joseph's subordinate in the Paper Office. He was not a Fellow Archer, but I felt it important to keep what could have been a promising friendship, alive.

The fact that my cousin and my old school fellow were both in London, cementing their friendship by exchanging information concerning our mutual friends and acquaintances in Herefordshire, often stirred my envy into anger. In the depths of restless nights I would ask God why had I not been born under the same star as that of Herbert Westfaling, when we shared so much more than the same Christian name?

He also enjoyed the companionship in London of another close to us, my younger brother Thomas. After several vain attempts to find employment and many letters to my father begging him to send money, he had been accepted as a salaried scribe by Messrs Clayton and Morris, the scriveners to whom many of our acquaintance had been indebted for loans. I met that intelligence with a mixture of relief and concern, concern that Thomas's slothful character would soon give Messrs Clayton and Morris reason to terminate his employment.

Allaying my fears and to my gratification, Thomas remained in their employ and proceeded to send me regular reports concerning the financial matters of the scriveners' customers and their friends. I now had a reliable and confidential pair of ears and eyes in the Capital.

At this time, Joseph was primarily occupied, among other things, as one of five Commissioners for seizing prohibited goods. He was also negotiating to be a contractor to manage the Royal Oak lottery, another lucrative position. As well, he had been called to the Bar from the Middle Temple, so I knew him to be a busy man.

So he was fast acquiring influence - and wealth - and in my heart his friendship meant much to me. I made sure to tell him in one of my epistles, that I rejoiced in his employment under so good a Prince, to remind him where my allegiance and that of my whole family lay – not only now, but also during the recent Troubles.

The words "Royal Oak" always lifted my spirits. The whole family celebrated Royal Oak Day, the twenty-ninth day of May, with great joy - the date now made an annual holiday of thanksgiving by His Gracious Majesty to mark, not only his birthday, but also his concealment in the famous oak tree at Boscobel so many years ago, and his arrival in London to take his rightful place as Monarch of these Isles.

There was even talk of instituting the Order of the Royal Oak, to acknowledge those who had devoted themselves to the cause of the Monarchy, and of course those who enjoyed an appropriate annual income. Many names were proposed for the honour, among them were many that displeased me, especially that of Sir Edward Hopton. With Cousin Herbert's name among them, I was convinced that my dear father would see 'Herbert Aubrey of Clehonger, Esquire' writ large in the list, and eagerly awaited news of this recognition of our family's loyalty. But to our great disappointment, the proposal to create this new Order withered on the vine.

To lessen our disappointment, my dear mother began working a cushion, carefully embroidering oak leaves on it, in silken gold thread. She and my sister Elizabeth worked on it together for long hours, a labour of love and loyalty. My mother left it to me in her will with explicit instructions that it remain at Clehonger Manor. I treasured it and her beautiful handiwork, executed with such devotion, for many years after her death.

I remember it well, the year the terrible plague struck London: 1665. At first, it seemed as if it would reveal itself to be just another visitation like so many others which, God willing, would soon abate. But when news came to us that thousands had been struck down and the King and Court were taking refuge in Oxford, our concerns overwhelmed us. A night-watch was put on the entrances to the city that I knew so well, to turn away refugees from the stricken capital. Thomas fled with Mr and Mrs Clayton to Middlesex. His Majesty and all our friends – and Thomas - were constantly in our prayers.

Joseph Williamson also followed the Court and always one to seize an opportunity, while he was there that summer, he entered into the printing and the distributing of official news. The production of rival news sheets was affected by the pestilence and by the time the Court returned to Whitehall, Joseph had acquired the monopoly of disseminating official intelligence. He called his publication *The London Gazette*. I was proud to call him my friend.

The Court with all its intrigues and gossip were a far cry from our rural community in Herefordshire. We thanked God once again that we had been spared the worst plague in living memory which carried off one in every six Londoners.

No sooner did His Majesty consider it safe to return to St James's, to the peal of bells and subdued rejoicing as we later heard, than in the following year, a terrible fire took hold and raged through the City, destroying most of it. Stories filtered through of this second devastation that came hard on the heels of the dreadful plague. Even His Gracious Majesty himself took charge of some of the fire-fighting and directed their operations in person. I found such accounts difficult to believe, but true or not, I thanked God for such a Monarch. The fire carried off only a handful of people, but it left thousands homeless and a City demanding to be rebuilt.

People said the terrible conflagration had been started by Papists, but in spite of the current frenzy, when people believed anything and everything they heard, I could not give credence to such nonsense. I took it upon myself to assure them that God had simply punished those poor people for their sins.

A few years after our daughter Joyce was born, to my great delight, my wife presented me with another son, whom I named Reginald, after one of the renowned early Aubreys, and as if to reward me further, I was made a Justice of the Peace, the position held by so many of my forebears. My position and reputation in the county was thus agreeably strengthened.

I had also heard that old Mary Rudhall, our great-aunt and the last surviving of William Rudhall's eleven children, was fast failing. Although she had numerous nephews and nieces to consider in her will, as her Godson, I looked forward with confidence to her remembering me with affection. Such an inheritance, when it pleased God for me to receive it, would ease my financial position considerably.

**

How he gulled me – and my dear Cousin Herbert Westfaling. Those who are pure in heart are often beguiled by the self-seeking. Roger Vaughan led me almost to ruin because I could see only the good in him. A personable young man with an unhappy past, Roger nevertheless betrayed my trust, not only mine, but also that of many others who endeavoured to help him.

At first, both Cousin Herbert and I felt sorry for our kinsman, his having been deprived of a father at a very tender age. He enjoyed a youthful charm that usually won people over, but I learned later, to my great cost, that his manner only reflected a shallow and insincere character. Roger acquired a reputation of a drunkard and spendthrift, but Herbert and I, who thought we knew him better than most, and understanding the circumstances of his childhood, would always defend him.

The position of the Herefordshire Receiver of Taxes had become vacant, so I wrote again to Joseph Williamson asking his interest and that of my Cousin Roger Vaughan, who had begged me to use what influence I could, to be considered for the position. Like me, he already enjoyed the position of Commissioner for Assessment.

Often, particularly when he was in his cups, Roger would relate the story of how his young mother met his step-father. She was Frances

Vaughan the widow of Henry Vaughan of Bredwardine and Moccas. A younger daughter of Sir Walter Pye of the Mynde, and thus my father's cousin, she was living with the child Roger at the time, in the Manor of Moccas.

'Old Tom the Keeper told me he discovered a man that he suspected was poaching deer in our Park – Moccas Park. He was hiding behind one of the big oak trees, the coward!' Roger took another long draught of my wine, as if to wash away the distasteful scene.

'Tom dragged the varlet inside to my mother, expecting her to punish him severely, which she should have!' Another draught and a signal for a replenishment. 'But he was hunting richer game!'

I had heard the story many times and so knew that to everyone's surprise, the 'poacher' was revealed to be Edward Cornewall, third son of John Cornewall of Berrington, a young man who had fought on the King's side during the Troubles.

At this point in the story, I would always applaud, but Roger's bitterness at his mother marrying the young man who had so blatantly forced himself into her presence, Cavalier or no, knew no bounds. His step-father now owned all the Vaughan estates and his new half-brother Henry Cornewall, would inherit everything that should have been rightly his.

When Roger was only about eleven, his step-father, married him to Anne, the daughter of Thomas Howard, Lord Arundel, a Royalist and

---

Sir Walter Pye = Joan Rudhall
(1571-1635) | (c1584-1625)
    Frances Pye = (1635) 1) Henry Vaughan of Bredwardine and Moccas
                                                          (1613-1701)

                                     |

                        Roger Vaughan (1641-1672)

            = (1650) 2) Edward Cornewall of Berrington (1613-1709)

                                     |

                    Henry Cornewall M.P. (c1655-1716)
                    Frances (b.c1659-) = William Lingen (b.c1657)
                    Mary (c1668-1702) = Gilbert Nicholetts
                                                   (c1666-1691)

---

lapsed Roman Catholic. She brought a dower of £4,000, two-thirds of which was sequestered for recusancy, the child being deluded enough to cling to her old faith. We could only sympathise with Roger's misfortune.

The union lasted less than five years and fortunately Roger did not succumb to the temptation of his young wife converting him to Roman Catholicism as they are always wont to do. Had he done so, his future would have been jeopardised; there being a justifiable and growing fear in many quarters that the Papists wanted to consolidate their forces and overrun the country.

After the war Roger married another Anne, the daughter of Sir Thomas Tompkyns of Monnington-on-Wye and Mary the daughter of Sir Walter Pye of the Mynde, making them cousins. She brought as a dowry, the hundred-year-old mansion at Weobley known as Garnstone that had been built by the girl's family.

When Roger broke the news to me one day that he had been forced to sell it, he could hardly utter the words. At first I could only sympathise with him, knowing that he was in straightened circumstances again, but I could scarcely believe my ears when he finally admitted that he had had no choice but to sell it to that detestable Colonel John Birch – the very same man whose Parliamentary forces had besieged Hereford sixteen years earlier and had caused do much havoc and distress.

That fact sorely tested our friendship, but when Roger confessed it to me, inebriated as he was at the time and with tears running down his face, I could only draw upon my vast reserves of Christian charity and forgive him. Not long afterwards, Roger came to call on me to tell me about an amusing plan he had just devised.

22. Speculation

I was living at Black Friars, just north of the city of Hereford at the time, needing to be closer to the hub of activities in my position as a Commissioner of Assessment. Roger was a fellow Commissioner, but in addition to that position, he had been appointed to the office of Justice of the Peace, young as he was. Being often in London, he would usually impart important information to me about noteworthy individuals in the county and the capital - after he had done justice to a bottle or two of my best wine.

So, always enjoying Roger's company, I was eager to learn what he had to say.

'I had a deuce'd run of bad luck with the cards,' he said with a smile, on this occasion. At that I expected him to ask me for a loan, but to my relief, he told me he had been forced to borrow from Nicholas Pitt, a kinsman of his step-father.

'And I gave him good security for the loan, I swear!' He re-filled his glass. 'But then, a rattling good idea came to me! I bet Mr Pitt that if I successfully reached the age of twenty-one, I would pay him £500, but if I did not, then he would get nothing!'

We both laughed at this amusing jape. 'Only one small detail stands in the way. I need three persons to stand surety for me.' He smiled winningly. 'Thomas Moreton and our kinsman Thomas Price have already agreed to do so – would you honour me by making up the third?'

The latter was seldom out of debt but he and his family were ardent Royalists, so I consented readily. I knew that soon Roger would come into his inheritance, which he told me was valued at about £1,500 a year and therefore he would easily be able to discharge the debt. Although he drank rather too much than was good for his reputation in the county, he was a healthy enough young man. We all laughed merrily at such a bizarre wager, as we signed the bond.

Some years later, Roger was made Captain of Foot of the Admiralty Regiment and Groom of the Bedchamber to the Duke of York. We all knew His Highness to have strong Catholic sympathies, but he was the younger brother of the King and as such, deserved our unquestioning allegiance and loyal devotion. Queen Catherine had failed to give her husband an heir and not infrequently, I would ponder on the future of the country if she remained barren. I could only pray for God's intercession and put such desperate thoughts from my mind.

Unfortunately, while at Court, Roger acquired a reputation of being 'a pitiful pimping bedchamber man to His Highness' as malicious gossips so cruelly put it. When these slanders filtered through to Hereford, as they invariably did, I resolutely defended the young man who had been through so much and whom I was still proud to call my cousin and kin.

Nevertheless, I fully expected that Roger's young half-brother Henry Cornewall, who had been appointed the Duke of York's Page of Honour would have a good influence on Roger. I did not want to believe that any kinsman of mine could be held in such ill repute.

It was not until much later that I heard that Roger's indiscretion had brought him into conflict with Henry Seymour, a groom of the King's Bedchamber. Seymour claimed that Roger had misrepresented one of his speeches to the Duke and challenged him to a duel. Honour was satisfied and both fortunately survived the encounter.

On one of his now infrequent visits to this county, Roger called on us to pay his respects to my wife. Joyce thought little of him, not liking his manners or his demeanour. She reminded me, as she was often wont to do, that her grandmother Margaret Vaughan was descended through the Vaughans of Tretower and that she considered Roger to be a disgrace to his name and lineage. I warned her against listening to idle gossip and told her she knew nothing of his unhappy childhood, and advised her to welcome him as a kinsman.

Roger wanted me to be the first to know that he had been appointed Receiver of the Herefordshire Hearth Tax. It was a position that I myself had suggested to Joseph Williamson, not once, but on a number of occasions. Nevertheless, I rose above such petty considerations as envy and willingly agreed to stand surety for him. I was reassured to learn that his other surety was his half-brother's uncle, Humphrey Cornewall, a Royalist, who had fought so bravely in the Troubles.

Imagine my great consternation, when in the following year I learnt that Roger had petitioned for the Hearth Tax to be put into receivership. Humphrey and I were now liable for £1,800, the sum Roger left owing the Crown. Ruin now stared me in the face and Joyce's bitter words on the subject did nothing to lighten my black moods. Herbert Wesfaling was similarly cursed; he was left bound to Roger for a loan of £1,000, for which he had stood surety.

I now saw Roger for the cowardly scoundrel he was. He ran from his responsibilities and his many other private creditors who were crying for their money, and fled the country. When the next war against the Dutch broke out, we heard that Roger had joined the Navy. At the battle of Sole Bay, shot from an enemy cannon found its mark and killed him. He met his Maker on the twenty-eighth day of May of 1672, leaving his affairs in a parlous state and his creditors in despair.

Such was the price of trust Herbert and I and his other kinsmen and had bestowed on Roger Vaughan. My own financial position was fast becoming desperate, but worse was to come. I had completely forgotten the amusing wager Roger had made those years ago before he had reached his majority, but I was sharply reminded of it when soon after Roger's demise, Nicholas Pitt came to see me.

Angry at learning of Roger's fate, Nicholas told me that the young man had never repaid his original debt taken out all those years ago, nor had Nicholas seen anything of the £500 after Roger had celebrated his twenty-first birthday. Nicholas wanted to be paid everything Roger owed and stated that I was liable for the debt – with interest – and he wanted the money immediately.

In vain I explained to Nicholas that I was temporarily embarrassed financially, but my pleas fell on deaf ears. Nicholas took me to court, as a consequence of which I was forced to pay him £100 as well as £12-10s legal costs and a further £70 plus interest from February 1673. At the same time Nicholas agreed to discharge the arrears on the bond against me and was made to swear he would not 'arrest, molest or trouble' me for a hundred years.

By then, we would both have met our God and accounted for our sins, but in the interim, fate had more tests in store for me.

Captain Henry Cornewall, petitioned the King for permission to sell Roger's lands to pay his debts to other persons to whom his estate was pre-mortgaged. He had taken it upon himself to untangle the web of debt and dishonesty that his half-brother had left to the world. Humphrey Cornewall, Henry's uncle and I did likewise, pleading that as Roger's sureties we would be ruined if process was executed on us for His

Majesty's debt. I prayed that Joseph might be in a position to help me, his having been recently honoured with a knighthood. We waited daily for His Majesty's gracious response.

***

Great-Aunt Mary was nearing the end of her life, and Joyce's father was ailing, yet in spite of expectations of an inheritance, my debt to the Crown as a result of Roger's dissolute and irresponsible behaviour still hung heavy on me. The fear of imminent ruin forced me to take to my bed for several days.

Rudhall Manor had fortunately been spared by the wretched Puritans, unlike Clehonger Manor. In several of our rooms, holes still gaped in floors and ceilings and plaster hung sadly on walls. My father always promised he would see to their repair, but somehow he shut the doors to them in his mind and my mother did likewise to them in fact, ordering the servants to leave the rooms untouched. And without Anne, I had no inclination to search out the condition of our 'priest's' hole. That belonged to our past and its terrible memories, those that I had seen and heard as a child during the Troubles, that I had often asked God to help me to forget.

On my last visit to Rudhall – I always made a point of visiting the old lady whenever I could, to enquire after her health - I had noted with satisfaction the beautiful tapestries and *objets d'art* and fine paintings that her eldest brother John Rudhall collected on his Grand Tour, and the large number of books in the library that had been accumulated over the years. The furnishings were as I remembered them as a small child, but the manor house itself was not nearly as immense as it once appeared to me all those years ago.

Cousin Herbert and his wife Ann had conveniently installed themselves in Rudhall Manor with their young children. The arrangement suited everyone, as Herbert spent many weeks at a time away in London and Old Aunt Mary, as we affectionately called her, now needed comfort, attention and companionship.

On one of my last visits to the old lady, Mrs Westfaling expressed her concern to me that on a number of occasions, a stranger claiming to be a Rudhall kinsman had come to the manor house. She related the details of these episodes to me, fearing for the safety of the old lady, herself and her children. His constant appearances at the door of the manor house, never when Herbert was at home, frightened Great-Aunt Mary greatly.

'He demanded to see Mrs Rudhall, but I liked not his manner or his looks, and so deemed it prudent to refuse his request.' I favoured her with a compliment to her good sense.

'Each time, he threatened to return,' she continued, 'and each time I ordered the servants to send him away, but the stranger always refused. The last time, only a few days ago, I had him forcibly evicted from the premises.'

She expressed gratitude that she could relate these events to a man of sense, asking for my advice, not wishing to concern her dear husband with them, he being so busy in London. I succeeded in allaying their fears, believing them to be simply irrational emotions so often visited upon the fairer and weaker sex, especially when living alone without the protection of a male.

Not long after Mrs Westfaling's encounters with the interloper, Great-Aunt Mary died, having lived a virtuous life and now mourned by her sisters' many children and grandchildren. On her death, my dear Cousin Herbert inherited Rudhall Manor at last, being the grandson of the eldest of old William Rudhall's daughters. His inheritance brought it home to me, all the more forcibly, that Fate had decreed that his grandmother came first in the line of females, while mine came fourth.

As to be expected, Great-Aunt Mary made Cousin Herbert executor of her will in which she left bequests to the offspring of all her sisters save those of Lady Pye and Mrs Broughton for reasons that my Cousin would not reveal. After gifts of monies to the poor, Herbert inherited the rest of her goods, chattels real and personal estate. In recognition of his inheritance, he named his son and heir Herbert Rudhall Westfaling.

Nevertheless, as I had hoped, Great-Aunt Mary left me two years' worth of rents and profits from the lease of lands in Brampton Abbots. She was a very wealthy woman and I could have done with much more, but I said an extra prayer for her soul in church the next Sunday, in thanks.

As has been so often been the case in my life, highs have always been countered by lows. We had no sooner buried the old lady, when someone by the name of Bartholomew Rudhall of the parish of St Giles in the Fields in Middlesex lodged a Bill of Complaint in the Court of Chancery.

He was the stranger who had caused Mrs Westfaling and Great-Aunt Mary so much distress. Now the old lady was dead at last, he claimed to be the next male heir of William Rudhall, and therefore the person who should inherit all the Rudhall property.

This Bartholomew Rudhall had the temerity to allege that he had been defrauded and deprived of his just inheritance by a will that 'pretended to be made', as he described it, by William Rudhall's sister Mary. He then accused its benefactors of designing to defraud him of all the manor and all the lands and tenements et cetera mentioned therein and demanded that they provide evidence of their right to inherit. He even asserted that before she died, Old Aunt Mary had promised him money if he would release his right, title and claim and go away.

Cousin Herbert and I knew all this to be a tissue of lies but it concerned us both greatly that we might be deprived of an inheritance that was rightly ours. Herbert was particularly worried as to the outcome, his having spent so much on his election to Parliament.

The thought of this stranger evicting him and his family from Rudhall Manor drove him almost to distraction. We both had much to lose if the man's false claim could somehow be proven.

When we challenged this outrageous demand in Court, Bartholomew Rudhall could show no evidence that he was in fact the rightful heir to the estate, nor could he produce any proof to this effect. So to our immense relief, the threat, real as it was at the time, came to nothing. Yet, even with the £1,650 from Joyce's marriage settlement and the rents from Great-Aunt Mary's bequest, my financial position still plagued me.

Soon after the Rudhall case, matters improved and my mood lightened, for I anticipated receiving another inheritance very soon.

23. Priors Court

Joyce had been born and bred at Priors Court in the parish of Dormington, an estate that once belonged to the Priory of St Guthlac. The old house demanded an onerous journey to it from Clehonger, even from Hereford. Travellers had to take the old winding road that led across the Rivers Wye and Lugg, often swollen and impassable during heavy rains.

There, away from the easy access to Hereford and its sometimes frivolous distractions, Joyce had grown up with her two sisters Margaret and Dorothy. In the early days of my courtship, I soon observed from the attitude of Mr and Mrs Brydges towards Joyce, that they appeared to favour her above her other sisters, a factor that raised her in my estimation.

Joyce in turn loved Priors Court where she and her two sisters had grown up, in harmony with two doting parents. After her marriage, she spent as much time visiting them as she could, taking the nurse and the children with her for them to admire, sometimes spending days there at a time, neglecting her wifely ministrations to me.

Dorothy, Mr Brydges' youngest daughter, had insisted on marrying Walter Thomas, a man of little consequence from Swansea and to her everlasting shame and regret, I believe it was without her parent's consent. In spite of that disrespectful behaviour, her father settled a generous sum of money on her, and Mrs Brydges pleaded with her husband not to cut her from his will, to which he agreed. I could only deplore his indulgence.

Such an act on her father's part, as I reminded Joyce, seemed only to condone Dorothy's conduct and presented a bad example for other young girls to follow. In time, she came to regret her wayward and reckless action and was forced to remove herself from her husband, whom she alleged mistreated her cruelly.

Margaret, the oldest of the three daughters, had married Thomas Carpenter of Chilston in Herefordshire. She died soon after the birth of her daughter Theodosia whose later behaviour caused tongues to wag and cast a blight on the family name.

As for Mr Brydges' last will and testament and my wife's

expectations in that regard, I knew the scope and content of it all too well, having been a party to all the discussions and a witness to it not long before he died.

Leaving an ailing wife and daughters among whom he wished to divide his estate, he deemed it essential that his wishes should be carefully realised by three kinsmen close to him, namely his distant Cousin Herbert Westfaling, Edward Cornewall of Moccas, Roger Vaughan's step-father, and his wife's nephew Robert Dobbins of Evesbatch.

Unfortunately, I could not make him see that as Joyce's husband, I should dispose of the one third of the rents of Priors Court for my wife myself, not put the responsibility of it in the hands of strangers, however dear to him. Nevertheless, he insisted on appointing these three to do the task for handling each of the three shares, for those of his two daughters: Joyce and Dorothy, and his granddaughter Theodosia Carpenter.

We discussed the fate of his servant Susan Hull at great length. She had been with the family since a child and had nursed and cared for the three daughters like a second mother. Her hands were gnarled and she found it difficult to walk, but he insisted on leaving her the large sum of £30 and one of his tenements in Ledbury. I reminded my father-in-law at the time, that a servant would surely not know what to do with such an amount of money and would probably only waste it, but the old man remained adamant. He dictated that on Hull's death, her legacy would go to my wife.

I had needs be content with that. Mr Brydges pointed out to me on a number of occasions that his remaining daughters Joyce and Dorothy were dearer to him than life itself and mollified me somewhat by assigning me with his other son-in-law Thomas Carpenter to be trustees of the other legacies.

Unhappily, Mr Brydges succumbed to a sickness that defied the constant ministrations of his doctors. I remember that Joyce was with child during the last weeks of her father's life and could not visit him as she begged to be allowed to. He met his Maker just before her lying in and I endeavoured to placate her hysteria by reminding her that it was God's will that her father should be taken from us without her paying her last respects. I named the boy she bore Brydges but even that act of kindness made no impression on her grief.

Her sister Dorothy had left her husband in Swansea in time to be with her father in his last days and to comfort her mother. Mrs Brydges refused to be consoled by the fact that her husband bequeathed her the rents of his other properties and that of the Court of Park in Ledbury. I felt it seemly to remind her of her husband's example of Christian behaviour in his will by forgiving his Cousin Marshall Brydges his trespasses, a kinsman with whom he constantly quarrelled, but such words from me did not succeed in lessening her sorrow.

My wife Joyce felt the loss of her father greatly, and appeared to show no interest in the fact that he had left me £100 and a further £100 to breed up young Herbert at Oxford. He left little Joyce £300, which was to be divided among any future children that my wife should give me in the future. This of course now included the baby Brydges.

As was only right and proper, my father-in-law had made me, together with Thomas Carpenter, executor of his last will and testament. The old man considered Cousin Herbert to be one of his most loyal and trusted friends and appointed him one of the overseers of his will.

To my consternation, the widow Brydges later agreed to marry old Dr Bridstock Harford. I did not hesitate to show my displeasure at this turn of events, even though Priors Court had been settled on my wife Joyce and her sister. I feared that the legacies my father-in-law left for his favourite daughter and our children, could be threatened by the new husband. As it happened, my fears were groundless, but the cloud that hovered over the immediate future of my family, gave me several sleepless nights.

After their marriage, Joyce's sister Dorothy went to live with her old servant Susan Hull in Ledbury, an arrangement that suited everyone. The death of first one parent and then the marriage of the other, not to mention the anguish and foreboding that union caused me, resulted in Joyce succumbing to melancholia and she was forced to take to her bed for several weeks.

One day, Paul Foley came to see me with a proposition. He was an acquaintance of some years standing and I knew that unfortunately, he held strong Puritan convictions. Nevertheless, people held him in high regard as a lawyer and he was recognised as a benefactor of some renown, having presented to the City of Hereford and its citizens, a contraption he called a 'fire engine'. He also contributed £20 per annum for the relief of the poor, all this as a result of his father having acquired a fortune in the business of manufacturing iron.

A tall young man with a direct, unblinking eye, he began by telling me how he came to have recently bought the large old manor house of Stoke Edith from the Lady Alice, widow of Sir Henry Lingen.

Unlike my poor father, who got nothing, the Lady Alice received a generous £10,000 from the Crown as compensation for the family's years of hardship, but her son died before he could revive the family fortunes. Like so many Royalists, Sir Henry's worth had been depleted by Parliamentary fines and generous contributions from his own pocket to the Royalist cause, and the maintenance of a regiment of horse. In spite of my condemnation of his actions to Cousin Herbert during the election to the Cavalier Parliament we could only mourn the passing of a devoted and loyal soldier.

Mr Foley came straight to the point.

'Mr Aubrey, do you not think that the time is perhaps right for the beneficiaries of Mr Brydges' will to sell Priors Court? I confess to you that I have long shown an interest in acquiring that property, lying as it does, some two miles south-west of my new abode, Stoke Edith.' He cleared his throat delicately.

'I have heard tell that you have recently found yourself in financial difficulties, largely through your generous support to a kinsman, ones I am sure will soon be settled.' Mr Foley held my gaze steadily and I could not deny his words.

'Besides,' he continued, 'one day in the not too distant future, I intend putting myself forward as a candidate to represent Hereford in Parliament. I have also heard that you too have expressed similar aims, Mr Aubrey. Such a purchase would thus serve the interests of us both.'

He then did me the honour of offering me a price for it and bade me consider it carefully. As I expected, Cousin Herbert and Edward Cornewall tried to dissuade me from accepting his offer, deeming it to be too low, but they both understood only too well the dire financial straits we were all in. Even Joyce's share of the rents from her father's will that she graciously put into my hands to ease my burden did not provide the relief for which I had hoped.

The amount Mr Foley offered was also less than my dear wife had expected, but it took little persuasion on my part to facilitate the agreement. Dorothy offered no resistance and my fellow executor Mr Carpenter had moved to London where he was raising his daughter Theodosia, so nothing stood in the way. I happily accepted Mr Foley's offer and he, being a lawyer, lost no time in drawing up the agreement to sell.

For some time afterwards, my wife persisted in reminding me of her opposition to the hasty sale of her family's old residence, but I put it down to her feminine frailty. The shock of her father's death and the obligation I felt to sell Priors Court after her mother's death, caused a change in her manner that I could only attribute to acute melancholia.

In her eyes, the fact that I sold it to Paul Foley whose family were iron-mongers and Presbyterians to boot, made it so much the worse. She could never understand that Mr Foley was a man who could smooth my way to Parliament.

My Fellow Archer, now Sir Joseph Williamson, had succeeded in getting elected as Member for Thetford, and my dear Cousin Herbert was already ensconced at Westminster. I knew I had as much to offer as they, but the path to London did not come cheap – and I do not refer to the newly imposed turnpike tolls that had everyone in the county a-grumbling.

A few years before Roger Vaughan met his Maker, my friends in London rewarded me with the position of Receiver of Taxes. I was honoured to be entrusted with such an undertaking, and I assured Sir Joseph – if I ever needed to – that my integrity would not disgrace my friends.

24. Woes Aplenty

For I had enemies, chief among them being William Bowdler, a conceited little Alderman of Hereford who coveted the position of Receiver himself and importuned many men of consequence in London for favours. But before that recognition of my worth and standing, then a reversal of my fortunes, in 1671, I suffered the loss of my dear father.

He lay grey and ill for many weeks before God took him from us. My dear mother went about her usual tasks with her accustomed dignity, aided and supported as always by our old servant Marie Dating and my sister Elizabeth. It was as if they needed no one else, just themselves, for solace. For some reason, my visits to my father's bedside, brief perforce as they had to be, and the vigil of my wife and children in his chamber, which I insisted on, did not give him the succour and comfort that I would have supposed.

At his funeral, our cousins, his friends, his tenants and his servants came to pay their last respects to the old Cavalier. We buried him under the floor of our local church, to whence, ever since I could remember, he would lead us all from Clehonger Manor down the drive, through the gates and across the roadway, so often covered in mud in the cold wet winter months, and into the old church to our family pew. At one time there were seven of us, dutifully filing behind our parents. Now we were a forlorn few, shuffling behind our father's coffin.

My sister Elizabeth, whom my father had left amply provided for and comfortably secure, insisted on being the one to support our dear mother through this melancholy ceremony. The pair were flanked by my two remaining brothers, Godwin and Thomas, to whom my father had each left £100. Godwin, his face tanned from his years in warmer climes, had returned to these shores from Smirna just in time to see our father before he died. Thomas, thoughtful and scowling, had always been on hand to help my father with the estates, before seeking work in London.

The old Cavalier had overcome so many obstacles with fortitude and faith and would always be an inspiration to me. I hoped too, that my sons would look upon their grandfather with pride. I penned the poem that we had engraved on a plaque and placed on the north wall of the church. It read:

In name (blest Soul though piously we hope
By Marble to preserve thy Memory)
Tombs have as all Things else, their Fate and must
Crumble into their Principals of Dust.
Thy Actions speak thee best by Life well spent
Is thy best Epitaph and Monument.

He made my dear mother his sole executrix and left her nearly all his property for her lifetime. To my sister Elizabeth went the lands, tenements, meadows and pastures in Snodhill Park south of Dorstone that he had acquired in 1664. To my dismay, the lands that he had bought from me, in the parish of Peterchurch, to ease my financial burden, he also left to Elizabeth, still a spinster and very much set in her ways. After her death, they were to go to my son and heir Herbert.

'Better the lands come to me and then to young Herbert, than to risk losing them all because of your – debts,' she opined with a nervous smile, reading the disappointment in my face on hearing this news. Nevertheless, I was forced to suspect that Elizabeth's constant attention to my father, especially on his deathbed, may have influenced his decision.

All this time, my huge and unexpected debts still hung heavy on me, as they did with many others who had been seduced by Roger Vaughan's charm. Daily I waited for a gracious response from our petition to His Majesty, but instead came letters threatening to bring legal proceedings against us in the Chancery Court of the Exchequer.

I wrote yet again to Sir Joseph, imploring him to help me. My old friend now enjoyed the position of Clerk of the Council in Ordinary. To my great relief, His Majesty discharged us from our surety bonds. Yet, somehow or other, even with that welcome reprieve, as the Receiver of Taxes, I still found myself owing the Treasury £1,548.

One person who took extreme pleasure in taunting me all through these difficulties, was that immoral man Colonel John Birch, who had lead the victorious Roundheads into Hereford, pillaging the town and desecrating our Cathedral. I never forgave, nor would I ever forget, that he and his like were responsible for so many of my family's woes.

Having bought Roger Vaughan's old estate Garnstone, and claiming to have shed his Puritan sympathies, Colonel Birch had earlier stood as a Member of Parliament for Penryn. He had enriched himself at the expense of many Royalists, and was now Commissioner for Excise, Trade and Wine Duties.

The King in his generosity had agreed to lease Colonel Birch fifty-five acres of land in Hyde Park in London to grow apples for cider in return for half the annual crop. The Treasury later decided to buy back the lease, before the first apple tree had even been planted, using the funds owing to it from the Hereford Hearth Tax. This is the money that I should have paid the Treasury, money that was now marked for the pocket of Colonel Birch.

The fact that I would have to face the man I despised most in the world and ask his indulgence to grant me an extension of the payment of this debt, gave me constant sleepless nights. In desperation I made what little economies I could. Against some local opposition, I had the Hereford town ditch drained and used it as an additional vegetable garden.

I mortgaged the tithes of Pearces Farm to John Wood of London for a paltry £100 – he would not give me more. The post of Coalmeter, superintending the measurement of coal was mine for £200 a year, which responsibility of course I devolved onto a person whose standing in the community was more in keeping with such a position.

Finally, with great reluctance, I sold Greyfriars, which I had rebuilt after its being almost demolished during the war, and with what it brought, I was able to pay some of the money still owing. The rest I hoped to find by levying a fine on part of my estate. My tenants in question were not overjoyed at having to find more money in addition to their rent, but I reminded them yet again, of their good fortune in having such a magnanimous landlord.

I wrote constantly to Sir Joseph, always making sure to thank him for his generous assistance and keeping him informed of my progress. I also reminded him that I would be eternally grateful if he could secure for me any position of a nature that would better enable me to make some return to all his favours. I knew that one such, a position in the household of the Archbishop of Canterbury was vacant, but it went to another.

A rumour came to me about this time, that some men of standing in the community had met in secret and had decided among themselves, who should represent Herefordshire in the next Parliament. My anger knew no bounds when I learnt that they had decided that one of the candidates was to be that wicked man, the very same Colonel John Birch, and that they had deliberately excluded my dear friend and Cousin, Herbert Westfaling.

I immediately alerted Herbert to this development for which he thanked me profusely, and wrote to Sir Joseph, giving him a full report, and ended:

Thus you can see what is the design of those that do not love the Church. No labour of mine shall be wanting to put a stop to the endeavours of those, who, I am confident would disturb the government. Communicate this to all your good friends in London.

Slowly I was acquiring the means to repay some of my debts, but in spite of my earnest of efforts, the Treasury became increasingly impatient. Their letters hinted that I could expect dire consequences if I did not pay the money they owed to Colonel Birch for the lease of the fifty-five acres of land in Hyde Park in London to grow apples for cider.

My blackest thoughts warned me of the precariousness of my position as a Receiver of Taxes. These overwhelming concerns and the dread of having to face that immoral man to whom I had to pay the money the Treasury owed him, brought on a renewal of my sleepless nights. As a result, I was forced to take to my couch for some days.

The noise of my children irked me and my wife's numerous suggestions that she considered helpful, brought no hope or comfort whatever. I could only entreat God to lift me from my slough of despond, but He failed to heed my prayers.

To add to my woes, another matter gave me grave concern. The King issued his Declaration of Indulgence. This allowed Dissenters to worship in licensed buildings and Catholics to perform their rituals in their homes without fear of reprisal, although the Test Act still meant they were excluded from holding any office.

Many saw the hand of the Duke of York in this. He was about to marry the Catholic Mary of Modena, his first wife Anne Hyde, the sister of Lord Rochester having died only a few years earlier. I feared for the survival of our Church in such inauspicious developments.

Then Thomas wrote a hurried letter from London with more unhappy news. All the Goldsmiths had received notice that the funds deposited by them in the Treasury had been confiscated and that repayment of the moneys advanced by them to the Exchequer would be discontinued. All of London was agog at this calamity. Many goldsmiths were compelled to suspend payment of interest to the people – not only merchants, but widows and orphans - whose money had been deposited with them.

One goldsmith was fortunate enough to have had the care of Lord Shaftesbury's money[1]. In confidence, His Lordship gave him prior warning of the imminent closing of the Exchequer, which allowed Mr Duncumbe (for that was his name) to withdraw very great sums of his own and £30,000 belonging to the Marquis of Winchester, before the axe fell.

Thomas kept me abreast of further developments: the King had directed that Sir Thomas Osborne[2] be appointed to clean up Augean stables and to restore London's mercantile reputation. Sir Thomas came from an old cavalier family from Yorkshire, so I knew that the Treasury would be in good hands. Gossips now whispered stories that the new Lord Treasurer, even though he enjoyed some eleven or twelve hundred pounds a year, owed more than ten, since having to maintain both his London establishment and his Yorkshire home.

My own financial state paled into insignificance compared to his misfortune and that of so many others, but even learning of his appointment to rectify the nation's plight, failed to lighten my black moods.

The terrible winter of 1676 froze the very marrow of our bones and sickness ruled the land. Joyce and even the servants complained constantly of frozen fingers and toes. Daily we learnt of yet another victim who suffered a burning fever and aching body on the way to meet his Maker. Many people of our acquaintance fell victim to that illness which in most cases, carried them off in a matter of weeks.

My dear mother was one of them. Feverish and weak, she failed to respond to any of the cures our doctor of physik recommended, not even to frequent blood-letting, but died on the twenty-first day of November.

Once again our family gathered at Clehonger, this time to attend the funeral of an exemplary wife and mother. She had comforted us all in those times of misfortune, she had striven to feed and clothe her children and even put her own food into our mouths, ever sacrificing her own well being for that of others.

As I never failed to remind Joyce on the numerous occasions she voiced her grievances, women who had not guided their Royalist husbands and their children through those strife-driven years of the civil wars knew nothing of adversity. My sainted mother, born and bred in London, the daughter of a rich and pious man, had suffered greatly in the course of her married life. With hardly a complaint or a womanly tear, she had seen our house destroyed, our property plundered, her personal possessions stolen – and her children weakened with hunger.

On the day of her funeral, friends and kinsmen, tenants and servants filled the familiar old church, shivering in the bitter cold with smoking breaths, to join us in mourning her loss. Coughs and sneezes and intermittent sobs punctuated the tolling of the bell and the old sin-eater's hands trembled as he went through the ancient ritual over her coffin. We laid her in the grave next to her husband. As to be expected, my sister Elizabeth wept loudest. Our old servant Marie Dating sat beside her with head bowed, sobbing into a piece of ragged cloth.

The entire parish mourned my mother, in particular the poor about whom she had always been concerned. In her will, she set aside £5 and directed that fifty poor women of the parish be given large coats of frieze with hoods of the same. In addition, every one was to have shoes and stockings and a flannel apron and each to be given a yard of linen cloth for their necks.

Not all of these old dames could fit into the church, and those who could not, were forced to remain wait outside All Saints, huddled together against the bitter north wind. After the service, many approached my sister and blessed their benefactor's memory for their warm clothes.

Meticulous to the last, she left £100 to my unmarried sister Elizabeth, even though she had received £200 from my father plus his property at Snodhill Park and land in the parish of Peterchurch. Elizabeth also inherited my mother's farm and lands in Brampton Abbots for the term of her natural life, after which, I was pleased to learn, they would come to me.

Her cross-stitch embroidery and fabric went to my sister Anne in London, but not the long cushion that my dear mother had so lovingly wrought with the oaken leaf in silk to commemorate the return of our

Monarch. That, my mother rightly specified, must come to me, and directed that it remain forever in Clehonger Manor.

As further evidence of her Christian charity, she bequeathed £10 each to the two servants who had been devoted to her for years and to each of the others, 40 shillings apiece.

Young Herbert inherited her watch with the silver case and all her diamonds. Needless to say, my young twelve year old son was considerably more excited with the watch than with the gems. I threatened him with its instant confiscation if he even so much as crossed me in any way.

One part of her will caused me some anxiety, especially considering my current financial difficulties. She directed that £50 be laid out to accrue an interest of £3 per annum. The first year the money was to clothe three poor old men of the parish of Clehonger with coats and hose of frieze and shoes and stockings. The second year the money was to clothe three poor old women and the following year, the sum was to be spent on the binding of a poor apprentice boy.

I nearly succumbed to the temptation of borrowing that £50, which I could have so easily done, being in such financial straits, but I valued my good name above all other consideration and resisted the idea. I had written numerous letters to Sir Joseph Williamson, begging him use his influence with the Treasury to give me an enlargement of the time to pay my debts. I had even levied a fine on part of my estate, an act of desperation hardly welcomed by my tenants.

Now in the meantime, the monies I now owed the Treasury increased significantly.

For some time before, John Davis, an old acquaintance of Edward Cornewall of Moccas, Roger Vaughan's step-father, had done him the honour of requesting his name as a surety, he having been appointed a Receiver of the Hearth Tax for Hereford. One day Mr Davis called on me. He needed a second guarantor and could I assist him in this matter? Knowing him to be a Royalist and a friend of Edward's, I readily agreed and signed my name to the paper.

My wife repeatedly voiced her opposition to this act of friendship, in very strident and unladylike tones, but I pointed out to her that Edward Cornewall, the husband of my Cousin Frances, would stand surety only for men of honour and integrity, and therefore, so would I. I heard her mutter the words, 'Just remember Roger Vaughan!' as she fled the room to escape my wrath.

Unfortunately, some little time later, Mr Davis called on me, his face grey with worry and confessed that by reason of 'several casualties', as he put it, which he could not explain, he found himself insolvent and owed the Treasury about £1,600.

He escaped from my presence before the significance of his words found their mark. Thanks to him, I now faced almost certain ruin.

1. Anthony Ashley Cooper, 1st Earl of Shaftesbury (1621-1683) fought for the Crown during the early stages of the Civil War, but then changed sides and became a member of Oliver Cromwell's Council of State. At the Restoration, he was pardoned by Charles II and was appointed Chancellor of the Exchequer in 1661.

2. Sir Thomas Osborne, later Lord Danby (1631-1712) M.P. staunch royalist and fervent Anglican, Treasurer of the Navy in 1668, a Privy Councillor in 1672 and Lord Treasurer (1673-1678).

He was known to make large profits from the sale of offices, and maintained his power by corruption and by jealously excluding from office, men of high standing and ability.

He was impeached for treasonable communications with the French and imprisoned in the Tower from 1679 to 1684 when Herbert wrote him a letter of commiseration.

A contemporary described him as 'the most hated minister, that has ever been about the King.' Lord Shaftesbury, certainly no friend, called him an inveterate liar, proud, ambitious, revengeful, false, prodigal and covetous to the highest degree. He married Lady Bridget Bertie, daughter of the Earl of Lindsey, his 'tyrant wife' who became the subject of innumerable lampoons.

25. My Lord Danby

O verwhelmed with despair, my faith in my fellow men, even those of like rank and persuasion, sank ever lower. I took to my bed again for several days but ere long, I received the notice that I had long awaited and dreaded: I was bidden to appear before the Treasury Board in London and explain myself. One small consolation gave me hope on receipt of this command: through my old friend Sir Joseph Williamson, I had made the acquaintance of Sir Thomas Osborne, now Lord Danby, Lord High Treasurer and Chief Minister and a man of great power and influence.

On one of my visits to London, Sir Joseph had done me the honour of inviting me to a function at his London residence, Winchester House in St. James's Square. I donned my best jacket and britches for the occasion, for I knew that he and his charming wife Lady Catherine, the heiress to the Duke of Richmond and Lennox were given to entertaining men of quality and I confidently expected to find myself among them. I was not disappointed.

Talk and laughter met me when I stepped inside the portals of Number 21. Many of the guests, some of whose faces I knew, wore the latest fashion of the haute monde, long periwigs and face patches and nearly all were bedecked with silken coloured ribbons. I must confess that I wished my own attire had been more resplendent. I stood for some time before my arrival was noticed and the announcement of my presence could hardly be heard above the noise.

After supper and a concert of music in the salon where Sir Joseph himself entertained us on the viols, he allowed me to make the acquaintance of Lord Danby and his wife Lady Bridget, the daughter of the Earl of Lindsey.

His Majesty had only a short time before, bestowed an Earldom on the great man and I lost no time in assuring His Lordship that all my friends in Herefordshire had rejoiced at the news of his elevation and with his choice of title of the Earl of Danby.

I found His Lordship to possess a pale face, marred by an old duelling scar, with a broad, high forehead, large staring eyes and a long nose. He received my compliments with a formal bow, expressing his brief thanks through somewhat tight lips but then smiled and kindly enquired of me how matters stood in my county. I eagerly took the opportunity to assure him of my and my family's loyalty and devotion to the Monarch, as I knew his has always been.

At that, we were interrupted by his wife. Lady Danby was dressed somewhat oddly in a floral gown with huge sleeves and around her forehead was wound a red spotted cloth. Her Ladyship was busy feeding a Spaniel puppy in her arms and talked at great length on all and any subject that caught her fancy. In a slight pause in her flow of words, I brought up the subject of Northamptonshire, as I understood it to be her country of birth.

'Indeed! 'tis a pity, Mr Aubrey you have never visited North-amptonshire in all your life! That surprises me, and in that case I pity you, for you have never seen a more agreeable place than the countryside there. I visit there whenever I can, and I advise you to do the same.' I was about to promise her ladyship that I would do everything in my power to correct such a serious omission, when she continued.

'And I suppose you must have seen Mistress Behn's[1] latest play, 'The Town Fop' at the Dorset Garden Theatre?' I had needs plead guilty on that count as well. She raised her eyebrows again.

'But all of London is talking of nothing else!' A tall man with sharp eyes and a ready smile, approached us. 'Ah my dear brother, and his little wife!'

The young lady on his arm wore a wan expression as if finding the evening something to be endured rather than enjoyed. Her Ladyship paused sufficiently for introductions to be made. He was the Honourable Charles Bertie whom I knew to be Secretary to the Treasury and had charge of the Secret Service account. I had just bowed, expressing my honour of making such an acquaintance when her dear friend, the Duchess of Lauderdale caught Lady Danby's eye and she wafted away, the puppy barking in protest.

Just then, a man dressed so plainly that I was immediately reminded of a Puritan and a woman I took to be his wife joined our little group. To my surprise, the Berties greeted them both with great delight, for the woman, Mrs Cole, was the mother of Mrs Bertie. Her husband, Mr Cole, stood quietly by as his wife enquired after her daughter's health and the conversation then lapsed into gossip involving families in Northamptonshire in which I had little interest.

Soon I was left alone, my mind full of the opportunities I had lost of drawing His Lordship out on a host of important matters that he had doubtless discussed with His Majesty.

Thus, when Lord Danby summoned me to London to justify my actions to him and the Treasury Board, I felt somewhat more sanguine about the ordeal than would otherwise have been the case. In addition, on my mother's death, I had inherited a property at Brampton Abbots the sale of which I was now negotiating. Just as soon as it was settled, I would soon be able to discharge most of my debt to the Treasury.

Once in London I took heart and stood before His Lordship and the other members of the Board with some degree of confidence. However, immediately I became conscious of the atmosphere in the chamber. His Lordship's countenance appeared even more severe and from the gravity of the expressions of the other Members of the Board, I knew I would have to throw myself on their mercy.

I took a deep breath.

'My Lords. I acknowledge that I have done ill and that I should have paid His Majesty in the first place, but only fate and unhappy circumstances have prevented me. However, the fact that I was ordered to pay the money to Colonel Birch and knowing the temper of the man gave me pause. In all honesty, I confess I believe he would have torn me to pieces.'

Their Lordships exchanged glances while I warmed to my theme. 'My Lords. I chose rather to trust His Majesty than to face Colonel Birch, the man who..' I decided it was unwise to elaborate, so with a bow, I humbly craved their pardon and commiseration and understanding.

My speech was met with a polite silence. A minute passed. Lord Danby cleared his throat and at a signal, Mr Bertie, who had been sitting with quill in hand at an adjoining table, rose from his chair and ushered me from their august presence. He closed the door of the chamber behind us and turned to me, his countenance solemn, but his eyes bright.

'I am sorry Mr Aubrey, that it should have come to this.'

I could find no words to acknowledge his pity. 'However,' he lowered his voice, 'I know that Sir Joseph Williamson, and others, are always obliged to learn how matters stand in Herefordshire, matters that affect us - here, you understand?' With a final hard look, he turned on his heel and strode away.

Judith Cullen = *1) Peter Tryon of Haringworth Northants*
(1626-1694)   *(1604-1660)*

   |

     Mary Tryon = *1) Sir Samuel Jones of Courteen Hall Northants*
             = *2) Hon.Charles Bertie son of Earl of Lindsey*

   = *2) Thomas Cole of Liss Hants (1622-1681) M.P.*

   |

   Judith Cole = *Herbert Aubrey III*

I knew not what to expect as a result of this meeting, but in a matter of only weeks after my return to Hereford, the answer came, forcing me to suffer the grossest of indignities. My position as Receiver of Taxes had been taken from me and given to another. Worse still, it went to a man whom I disliked and distrusted, William Bowdler, the little Alderman from Hereford.

For months now, nay years I believe, he had been using his influence to denigrate me, spreading stories of a nature to bring down my reputation in the county. I knew that he intended standing for Parliament and I resolved to do my utmost to foil his attempt. I am happy to report that in that respect at least, I was destined to be successful.

In March the following year, with great difficulty, and to my relief, I was able to sell some of my land and finally to discharge a good part of my debt to the Treasury. This had been largely thanks to Mr Bertie, with whom I now corresponded on a regular basis. Through his good offices, Lord Danby was persuaded to facilitate a Bill though Parliament for the sale to occur. My gratitude to the great man knew no bounds.

All this time, momentous events were unfolding in the seat of power, demanding the attention of His Lordship who was playing a not inconsiderable part in them. I shall never forget that I was able, in my own humble way, to bring a crumb of comfort to His Lordship in the misfortune he would soon encounter.

During the time my Lord Danby was overseeing the nation's finances, he was also quietly influencing the course of future events by negotiating a marriage settlement between two impeccable Protestants, the Duke of York's daughter Mary and Prince William of Orange. We had long since given up hope of His Majesty begetting a legitimate heir, which meant that his Catholic brother James would inherit the Crown of England. Regardless of his beliefs, the Duke of York was His Anointed Majesty's lawful successor and it behoved all of us to acknowledge the Divine Right of Kings.

Yet in my heart of hearts, such a prospect, that of serving a Catholic King, filled me with dread. I was as secretly concerned as the next man when I reflected on the succession of the throne. To tell the truth, this growing crisis placed me on the horns of a terrible dilemma. Should I adhere to my faith in the Church of England, so wonderfully sculptured out of Roman dogma, extirpating that devil incarnate the Pope, and in so doing, betray my beliefs and swear allegiance to a Catholic King? Or should I remain loyal to the Crown and watch Catholicism take root in the land like some noxious weed?

My faith in the principles on which the Church of England was founded in Tudor times: the Apostles' Creed and the Thirty-nine Articles of Faith in particular had sustained and supported me throughout my life. I and my family had served our King and suffered for his cause without question, but I knew in my heart that a Catholic King would breed social anarchy and civil conflict, even worse than the one so recently brought about by Parliament and their Puritan supporters. I also feared that one day, I would have to proclaim publicly my choice to the world.

Times were rife with rumours and even in rural Herefordshire, people talked of Jesuits swarming all over the countryside in vile disguises. Many spoke of replacing the Duke of York with the Duke of Monmouth, one of the King's many illegitimate sons, to ensure a Protestant succession. They believed that Catholics were determined to murder the King and install his brother James to forestall such an eventuality.

Feeling ran so high, that people formed themselves into groups with the sole aim of removing the King's brother from the succession. They called themselves 'Exclusionists' and exhorted people to sign petitions. I was horrified that people had such temerity to think they could alter the succession to the throne of England – even under such dire circumstances. Some wit said they were nothing more than horse drovers or whiggamores, and the name, appropriately abbreviated, stuck.

Lord Danby's plans to negotiate the marriage of Mary to her cousin William finally came to fruition. Louis the Fourteenth of France naturally objected, but the nuptials were held on the twenty-first day of

October 1677. In spite of the possible consequences, I prayed that with God's help, this union might somehow forestall the calamitous outcome that so many of us feared.

In the course of all these negotiations, Lord Danby had made himself exceeding unpopular with the House of Commons. Every move he made in the nation's interest was cast in the most sinister of lights. His Majesty still held him in high esteem and even agreed to the marriage of his natural son the Earl of Plymouth to Lord Danby's daughter Bridget, named for his wife.

Lady Danby herself also became the target of abuse by the pens of the pamphleteers. Stories abounded, illustrated with unflattering drawings of Her Ladyship and her dog. Such unmannerly behaviour only cast a blight on Parliament and even the Court itself, as talk of His Majesty taking monies from the King of France, quickly circulated.

After that, matters came to a head and people were whipped up into a frenzy of anti-Papal accusations and denouncements. Rumours and counter rumours swept the land, each adding its weight to the developing crisis. We heard it confirmed that with Lord Danby's agreement, the King had received huge subsidies from the French King. I found this difficult to believe, but I knew that if it was true, then My Lord would have had good reason for his actions.

Then came the revelations of Titus Oates and his accusations of a Papal plot that swept up in its wake the guilty and innocent alike. It soon became apparent that the frenzy offered a perfect opportunity for foes to strike at any innocent victim. And so it happened to my Lord Danby.

Like all great and influential men, he had acquired many enemies and his lack of popularity, nay, even hatred in many quarters, worked against him. His relationship with the King failed to protect him from the malice of many in the House of Commons and seemed only to exacerbate it. Members drew up articles of impeachment, and he was forced to resign as Lord Treasurer. In spite of the efforts of the King to pardon him officially, he was committed to the Tower and even refused bail.

When I heard this depressing news, I thought long and hard. How could I ease the burden of the man who had for so long, been so powerful? One who had always endeavoured to serve Cavalier and Church interests? One who had been unremitting in his kindness to me? I immediately instructed Joyce to make ready a rolled and pressed piece of pork and to tell me when the next batch of cider would be ready, and put pen to paper.

1679, December 29. Hereford. When I consider the favours I have received from your Lordship, I stand amazed to think you could do so much and I merit so little. I must needs own my being to my God, but next to Him my preservation and all that little family that relates to me, to yourself alone, for without your generous assistance I would have been inevitably ruined.

Thus far you have trod in the great Strafford's[2] steps, may the great God of Heaven help you avert his fate and make you the support of our government and our nation's great preserver. Had I the power of persuasion and could from the abused world gain a credit equal to the value I have for you, I should not leave one ill thought in any doubting breast, but fire all hearts with a regard and honour for you. For this is my bosom filled above the reach of malice or envy to alter or corrupt. This have I lived, since I knew you, and this will I die.

Postscript. I beg the favour of your Lordship to present my most humble service to my Lady, to whom with yourself I wish a happy new year and many more. I have sent your Lordship a small collar of brawn, being deceived of a better, be pleased to accept it. As soon as ever our cyder grows fine, I shall make you a tender of some of it. I have committed this letter to my own brother that it may come safe to your hands.

Godwin had taken it upon himself to leave these shores once more, only returning briefly for our father's funeral, which meant that I had to rely on Thomas to deliver my letter secretly, fearing that such a correspondence might further incriminate Lord Danby.

Thomas was loath to do it, but I promised him I would refund him any coinage he might have to spend in order to persuade the Tower guards to let him into My Lord's presence. In the event, Thomas went there and quite openly gave him the letter, being allowed into his presence without any hindrance. My Lord graciously thanked Thomas for his pains and said that as he was feeling rather poorly, he looked forward with pleasure to the cider and collar of brawn.

Lord Danby languished in the Tower for five years, penning letters in code to his loyal friends and writing pamphlets and tracts, desperately trying to secure his freedom. Nevertheless, at least I had the satisfaction of knowing that I had alleviated his distress in no small way. I had written him words of comfort and kept my word about the collar of brawn and cider, which I made sure was safely delivered to him.

1. Aphra Behn (1640-1689) dramatist and novelist. Baptised at Wye in Kent, she was taken to Surinam as a child by her father. There she learned the history of the African prince Oroonoko, whose adventures she captured in the successful novel of that name.

Back in England, her wit and abilities brought her to the attention of Charles II who employed her on secret service during the Dutch war.

After that, she supported herself by her writing. Her many successful plays included the *Forced Marriage, or the Jealous Bridegroom*; *The Amorous Prince*; *The Town Fop*; and *The Roundheads*.

2. Thomas Wentworth, Earl of Strafford (1593-1641). One of King Charles I's most able advisers. Strafford was beheaded to great popular rejoicing – a supremely tactless reminder to Danby of the man and his fate.

26. Robert Pye of the Mynde

Unhappily, my Fellow Archer Sir Joseph Williamson was also committed to the Tower in the course of the terrible anti-Papal hysteria but His Majesty speedily ordered his release. Even so, my old friend found it necessary to relinquish his position as Secretary of State and Sir Leoline Jenkins[1], a long time associate, succeeded him. According to Thomas, whose ear was always to the ground, Sir Joseph had paid £6,000 for the post of Secretary of State and charged his successor the same amount when he left it. True or not, this did not lessen my admiration for either of them.

Both men had represented Britain at the Congress at Cologne that had helped bring about the peace between England and Holland. Stories abounded, telling of ill-feeling between them but I refused to listen to such tales. It gratified me that being a Welshman, a High Churchman and a Royalist, Sir Leoline and I had much in common. I am happy to add that like me, the new Secretary of State held a sincere belief in the Divine Right of Kings.

Having done what little I could for Lord Danby, I busied myself with my responsibilities as Justice of the Peace. The duties of this office were burdensome and without pay, but were essential in the overseeing of county affairs and reporting local opinions – and unrest - to Whitehall. Such duties were expected of men in my position, we who were born to serve the community. I had also been made Chairman of the Quarter Sessions, a position which required the legal qualifications that my father had so wisely urged me to acquire at Gray's Inn.

I lamented the fact that my own son and heir showed such little aptitude for study or politics, and I never failed to remind him of my displeasure when I witnessed daily, evidence of his manifold failings. Unhappily, my words of wisdom always fell on deaf ears. In spite of all my remonstrances, his mother invariably took his side, displaying an unhealthy indulgence towards him. I knew that her weak obstinacy in this regard would undermine the boy's character and encourage a lack of probity and rectitude. I predicted a future for him that boded ill.

By now he had struggled out of boyhood and emerged into man's estate. Unfortunately, he had persisted in acquiring a mind of his own, and many's the time I had to take a strap to him to remind him of his filial obligations. His mother took his side still, in spite of the lectures I gave her on the importance of a son obeying his father.

I saw to it that he completed his schooling, and told him that the path to his future lay through the portals of Queen's College, as mine had done. He expressed no enthusiasm – or gratitude - in accepting the opportunities I struggled to provide for him. To my despair, he espoused little or no interest in our Church, or the faith that had sustained me through so many difficulties. He seemed unable, nor in fact even interested, to answer the questions on the sermon I made a point of putting to the children after every church service.

Reginald on the other hand, although younger, would struggle to find the words that would tell me he had listened attentively to what had been said. He would lisp his childish replies and smile winningly at me when his answers were not as they should have been. Brydges always endeavoured to find favour with me by repeating the words of his older brother Reginald, even though he knew not what they meant. Young Joyce, a serious child, devoted herself to helping my wife with Betty, the baby we named Elizabeth, after my mother.

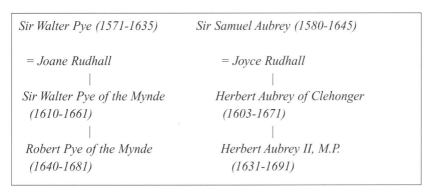

Sir Walter Pye (1571-1635)	Sir Samuel Aubrey (1580-1645)
= Joane Rudhall	= Joyce Rudhall
Sir Walter Pye of the Mynde (1610-1661)	Herbert Aubrey of Clehonger (1603-1671)
Robert Pye of the Mynde (1640-1681)	Herbert Aubrey II, M.P. (1631-1691)

In the winter of 1679, my bachelor uncle, the old Cavalier Anthony Aubrey died after succumbing to an illness punctuated by a succession of coughs and fevers. Over the years, we did what we could for him, but he insisted on living alone in genteel poverty, his meagre means augmented by the £20 a year as arranged in my father's marriage settlement and an annuity of £35. The latter sum came from Robert Pye, a kinsman and I am proud to say a fellow Queen's College man.

Robert Pye's Aunt Alice had married Sir Henry Lingen, at whose side my uncle had fought so gallantly. Robert's admiration for him and Sir Henry, and the unremitting efforts of these two old Cavaliers in the Royalist cause had prompted his generosity, for which I never failed to thank and bless him.

It pained me to remember that my grandfather, Sir Samuel, had bequeathed to his son only a confusion of debts, which my father had been obliged to settle. Then the Delinquency Fine forced my father to borrow more money and he still had to find £20 per annum for his brother.

In contrast, fate had smiled on Robert Pye. His elder brother Walter had embraced Catholicism, forsook his family obligations and retired to France, leaving Robert to inherit the Mynde, the seat of the Pye family for generations. How much more fortunate was Robert, being born a second son, than was I, and how much greater his inheritance!

People used to say that his grandfather, Sir Walter Pye of the Mynde, the husband of my grandmother's sister Joan, was the richest man in England and now, because of a fortunate marriage, Robert had as a father-in-law, Sir James Drax, one of the wealthy elite of Barbados. As a result of his marriage to Meliora Drax, Robert increased his land holding by acquiring valuable property on that island.

Sir Walter Pye of the Mynde (1571-1635) = Joane Rudhall (c1584-1625)
       |

1. Sir Walter Pye of the Mynde (1610-1661) = Elizabeth Saunders
   |

   Walter Pye [Baron Kilpeck] (d.1690)
   Robert Pye = Meliora dau Sir James Drax of Barbados (d.1699)
   (1640-1681)
        |

        Elizabeth (1678-1709) = Henry Gorges M.P. (c1665-1718)

2. John Pye (1620-1701) = Blanche Lingen of Stoke Edith
   |

   Edward Pye (1646-1696) = Anne Snell of Maryland

Sir James and his brother William Drax held large tracts of land there on which they planted sugar, harvested by the slaves who had been brought to the island to work on the cotton and tobacco plantations. Sir James even had shares in two slave ships that regularly brought the labour to work on his and other sugar plantations.

According to Robert, the manor house in Barbados known as Drax Hall was one of the most impressive on the island. It stood, he said, as a monument to the fortune Sir James was making in the getting of slaves and the exporting of sugar home here to England, an amount he claimed totalled some thousands of pounds.

The countries of the New World still lured many away from hearth and home; those who were willing to submit themselves to untold privation and I suspect, terrors on the high seas where storms and Spanish pirates waited to prey upon them and send them to a watery grave.

My brother Godwin was one such adventurer, always searching for the gold at the end of the far-away rainbow. My wife's cousin, William Brydges was another; he lived and traded on that distant island of Barbados before dying there at the age of twenty-three, a fact that I warned my sons to remember.

But I also know many who had no need to leave these shores to enjoy a share in riches that were there for the taking. Sir Joseph Williamson had stock worth £500 in the Royal Africa Company, but unfortunately, he failed to alert me to its formation so I was unable to avail myself of the opportunity to invest in such a lucrative proposition, even had I been able to borrow the money to do so.

Another of my slight acquaintance and closer to home, a wealthy merchant by the name of Captain Ferdinando Gorges held twice that number of shares in the Royal Africa Company. He came from Barbados and was acquainted with Sir James Drax. Unfortunately, the man had Puritan leanings and associated with the likes of Colonel Birch and Sir Edward Harley whom I heard, he entertained lavishly at his new manor house at Eye.

Young Thomas Coningsby of Hampton Court married Captain Gorges' daughter Barbara. A proud and haughty woman with a fiery temper, she never failed to remind us of her father's financial successes on the few occasions we chanced to meet.

Mr Coningsby did not seem to mind that his wife's father made his money from sugar and slaves and that people called him the 'King of the Blacks'. An ancestor of her father and a namesake, Sir Ferdinando Gorges, once held a vast swathe of land in America they call New England. His grandson inherited the land and sold it to the Massachusetts Bay Company for £1,250.

Stories of such riches, especially those so easily inherited, always held my sons in thrall, but I never failed to remind them of our kinsman's exemplary generosity of spirit by giving the annuity, and his recognition of the role that Cavaliers like my uncle and Sir Henry Lingen played in those past Troubles.

Robert Pye and his wife Meliora travelled all the way from the Mynde to attend Uncle Anthony's funeral. We and our other kinsmen paid our final respects to one of the last remaining Cavaliers who had seen service in the civil wars.

At his wake, my son Herbert, now aged fifteen, urged us to tell him once again how my grandfather had been taken as a prisoner and imprisoned in Bristol, and how we had withstood the siege of the Scots army at Clehonger Manor for six long weeks. The boys had heard the stories of the war many times, but I am proud to say, the tales never failed to impress them.

It fell upon me to administer my uncle's estate, little enough as it was. Apart from his annuities from his father and from Robert Pye, his only other asset, his wearing apparel, was valued at £3. I learnt later, that he had been forced to sell his sword, a treasured item that I had hoped that one day would come to my son and heir, for him to use to defend his honour if and when the need ever arose.

Not long after the death of my Uncle Anthony, Robert Pye himself unexpectedly went to his Maker. The shock of the young man's sudden death at a relatively early age rebounded throughout Hereford.

Unhappily he left no sons to carry his name, only a three-year-old daughter called Elizabeth to whom he was devoted. She would now eventually inherit the Mynde, the seat that had been in that family for generations and from whence so much Royalist support had come during the Troubles.

My wife expressed the hope that her mother would not remove the little girl to her father's place in Barbados and for once I had to agree with her. Yet it seemed likely, for Robert's brother Walter lived in France as Baron Kilpeck having eschewed his proper religion and his lineage. His cousin Edward Pye, the son of his Uncle John, dwelt across the seas in Maryland in America, which left the widow's closest male relative, her father, Sir James Drax, away in Barbados. At every opportunity, my wife speculated on the child's possible future and the terrible position in which Mrs Pye found herself until I commanded her to desist such idle chatter.

Tongues were soon wagging and people of little knowledge quickly spread stories as to the cause of Robert's death and its consequences. People said that he died as a result of wounds inflicted on him by one John Bodenham in a fracas stemming from the latter's refusal to take the Oath of Allegiance. Such was the explanation of Robert's demise that circulated within days of his passing.

A Royal Proclamation had required that all Roman Catholics take an oath of Abjuration and Allegiance before the magistrate of the Quarter Sessions in Hereford. Bodenham was a staunch Roman Catholic but he and Robert were also friends and close neighbours and I knew the explanation that had been put about, to be a tissue of lies. It behoved me to ensure that my friends in London were given the true story.

Worse still, the sorry and false account was perpetuated by two newsletters, no doubt with the aim of increasing their readership by stirring up anti-Catholic feeling. I took it upon myself to write to Sir Leoline Jenkins[1] the new Secretary of State, correcting its gross falsities and giving him a faithful state of the whole sorry business.

Last Easter sessions Mr Pye, Mr Edward Jones and Mr John Scudamore were ordered to tender the oaths of allegiance and supremacy to Mr John Bodenham, who had declined to take them. They accordingly issued out warrants. The constables made return that they were abused and had stones thrown from the house at them and were threatened and sued. Mr Pye met Mr Bodenham near his own house at the Mynde and told him of his refusal to take the oaths and of the abuses done to the officers and of the obligation on himself to make the order obeyed and pressed him to give security to appear at the next Sessions, which he refusing, Mr Pye said he would not let him go. Though he had nothing in his hand abut a walking stick he persisted in endeavouring to take him, but Mr Bodenham struck at him with a bill and hit him on the arm and broke his coat. Mr Pye fell, but confessed he had no great hurt.

After this Mr Bodenham promised Mr Pye to appear at a certain day, but did not come, and sent him word he was not obliged to keep his word with him. As Mr Pye since informed me, Mr Bodenham left the country on it and never saw Mr Pye alive from that time till his death.

The manner of Mr Pye's death was this. On Saturday the 22nd of January, he came in the morning to Hereford. He was very well and cheerful. He was pretty late with some of his friends and rode home in a very cold night and sickened in a day or two. Three doctors attended him, but his fever increasing put an end to his life on the 30th. He was buried on Candlemas Day and the very person said to murder him was one of his bearers.

Two of the doctors agreed that he died of a malignant fever and Mr Fielding said his lungs were immersed in blood. This is as true an account as I can give till I send his deposition, but what relates to his sickness, death and burial is certain. Such unreasonable gross lies will do great harm. This you may impart as you see cause.

Such were the matters of local import that I felt duty bound to report to London.

Robert's many cousins, friends, acquaintances and his tenants attended his funeral, all grieving for the loss of an honourable and upright man. I noted with disquiet Captain Gorges in deep conversation with the young widow with the little Elizabeth at her side both dressed in black and I pondered on the influence he might exert on her at this time.

My sons were also saddened, for they held Robert in high esteem, mainly because of the stories with which he would regale them. Young Herbert in particular, always importuned our kinsman, begging him to tell them about the country across the seas where his wife was born, where he had visited and where his father-in-law held extensive tracts of land.

'The island of Barbados lies far across the ocean, its brown and green hills rising up past white sandy beaches, lapped by blue crystal waters,' Robert would begin, his eyes absorbed, looking in his mind at the distant scenes he loved so well. He would tell them of the times that Spanish pirates tried to conquer the island that they called 'bearded' after the strange species of tree found only on the island.

Robert, however, had one tale that never failed to fascinate them. 'During the war, my great-uncle, Sir Robert Pye of Uptons, shot at one Captain Carlo Fantom, a Croatian,' he began. This way, he immediately had the boys' undivided attention.

'The missile went right through his buff coat, and to my great-uncle's astonishment, instead of keeling over wounded and in pain, Captain Fantom merely took the bullets from his arm and said, 'Here, take them and use them again.' Those who witnessed the exchange, stood still, transfixed. When pressed for an explanation, the Captain boasted that keepers of the Croatian forest knew a certain herb that when consumed, made them impervious to bullets.'

Naturally, my sons wanted to know the name of this wonderful herb, but Robert would just smile and promise he would reveal the secret in good time. I was particularly pleased when Robert never failed to finish the story by telling us that Fantom quarrelled easily, probably thinking he had a charmed life, and ended up by being hanged for ill-using women. I always advised my sons to ponder on this lesson.

Now Robert Pye was dead and they were doubly distressed when they realised the name of the miraculous herb had died with him. I told them that God had meant it to be, and they should remember to pray for his soul.

The Widow Pye remained at the Mynde, grieving with her little daughter. It concerned me to hear that a number of men of doubtful quality were commiserating with her loss and visiting the Mynde on many more occasions than a mourning widow warranted.

I prayed that she remain vigilant and be ever conscious of the religious leanings and loyalty of any future suitor after the hand of herself or her daughter – and the estate of the Mynde with its proud history of Royalist support.

1. Sir Leoline Jenkins (1623-1685) M.P., lawyer and diplomat. An ardent Royalist, he was also a Fellow of Jesus College Oxford of which he was Head before becoming an M.P. In 1680 he became a Privy Councilor and Secretary of State. He left most of his property to Jesus College and his books to its library.

27. Men of Influence

Iknew only too well the frailty of women, especially when suffering the lack of a firm hand in their upbringing. This was brought home to me when Joyce gave me the news that her niece Theodosia, the sixteen-year-old daughter of my wife's deceased sister Margaret had run off with Lemuel Kingdon, Deputy Paymaster of the Forces.

Mrs Carpenter died when the child was but young and Mr Carpenter saw fit not to remarry. The girl thus grew up in her father's house in London, without proper parental direction, cared for only by a series of governesses. As a result, she developed into a precocious child, the sole heiress of her father's estate. Two years earlier, through a kinsman of my wife, Mr Kingdon made the acquaintance of young Theodosia.

According to my wife, who made it her business to know such details, Lemuel Kingdon found no approval in Mr Carpenter's eyes even after numerous visits to his house of both a social and business nature. In spite of Mr Carpenter's displeasure, the young man secretly and persistently wooed Theodosia until she agreed to marry him.

Finally they eloped and we later learned that the young miss gave her age on the marriage licence as eighteen when in fact at the time, she was still only sixteen. She also claimed that she had the consent of her mother when Mrs Carpenter had been dead for years and as far as we know had never met Mr Kingdon. The whole episode greatly distressed my wife. She railed against the man who had so obviously worked his way into the child's confidence and encouraged her in this deceit.

Naturally I would never stoop to condone such actions and I could only lay the blame for the deceit squarely on the young hussey's comportment and lack of careful upbringing. My wife steadfastly refused to agree with me. Theodosia had been bereft of a mother's guidance and in her poor judgement, she had been led astray by the man's charm and good manners. Joyce vowed never to trust Mr Kingdon in any respect ever more. I pointed out to her that he was now a kinsman and that she should welcome him as such.

She vowed she would never do so, but I ignored her hysterics and cautioned her to think otherwise, for I had heard tell of young Mr Kingdon. His father, Richard Kingdon who had only just died, had been the Auditor of Army Accounts. According to Cousin Herbert Westfaling, Mr Kingdon had been part of Lord Ranelagh's syndicate to farm the Irish Revenues and he held the position of Controller of Prizes during the second Dutch war, in which His Majesty's brother the Duke of York had acquitted himself so honourably.

On old Mr Kingdon's death, his son lost no time in taking over his father's position as Deputy Paymaster of the Forces which allowed the young man to move into his father's influential and moneyed circles. I believed that Lemuel's birth and background and his father's achievements could only inspire confidence and admiration.

As fate would have it, not long after that, Mr Paul Foley called on me with a proposal that swept all else aside. He confided that he intended to stand for the next Parliament.

I remember him looking a little embarrassed as he continued,

'If no hindrances – of a financial nature – stand in your way, and your esteemed friends in Whitehall agree, I suggest that you and I stand as the two candidates for Hereford in the next election when His Majesty deigns to call one'.

His words lifted my spirits and I was more than honoured that he should thus seek me out. Joyce was quick to voice her disapproval of the man and everything about him, but I knew this meant that the time would soon come when I too would serve my King as a Member of the House of Commons at Westminster.

While endeavouring to keep the peace in Hereford, I continued to pen regular accounts to Sir Leoline Jenkins pertaining to local matters of great importance to him. These he invariably answered in the kindest of manner. The new Secretary of State enjoyed the reputation of being a most learned, rational and incorruptible man. I myself, having qualities of a similar nature and being his regular corespondent, could only concur with the general report of his character.

Yet one concern of utmost significance overshadowed all others and remained uppermost in everyone's thoughts: the future King of England.

Queen Catherine had sadly failed in her duty to give His Majesty an heir, although he had generously acknowledged a number of bastards, the Duke of Monmouth being considered the most senior. Nevertheless without a legitimate heir, only His Majesty's Catholic brother James could succeed him.

The burning question of whether a Catholic King could sit on the throne of England or not, caught fire across the country. To exclude the Duke of York, as so many misguided men wanted, I considered to be tantamount to a mortal sin. True Royalists soon termed these people 'Exclusionists' – a name that for me took on all the connotations of betrayal and treachery. In the course of endless debates and often heated arguments, I became even more firmly committed to the belief that only James, Duke of York could legally, spiritually and morally, rightly succeed His Majesty as the next King of England.

A number of influential persons believed the solution could be found only by the Duke of Monmouth succeeding his father. I even gave this notion some thought. I could see that he possessed many of the essential qualities of Kingship; he had fought with gallantry against the Dutch, his father had treated him like a son, he displayed a handsome mien – and he was a Protestant, which counted most in his favour above all other considerations. Nevertheless, nothing could alter the fact that the Duke was illegitimate, in spite of his mother Lucy Walter's insistence to the contrary.

My wife ventured to suggest that the Duke of York's daughter Mary should succeed her uncle, she being the daughter of the Duke of York by his first wife Anne Hyde, the sister of Lord Rochester the Earl of Clarendon and a Protestant, if only a woman could sit on the throne of England. I treated this idle thought with the disdain it deserved.

His Majesty had dissolved the last two Parliaments because a Member had dared to introduce a Bill to exclude the Duke of York from the succession. Both times, His Majesty immediately dismissed the Assembly and bade them all return to their hearths and homes.

In 1681, we anxiously awaited the King's summons for the next Parliament to meet. In the two previous assemblies, Mr Paul Foley and Mr Bridstock Harford had represented the city of Hereford when in both, the Exclusionists had endeavoured to do their worst.

The year before, young Mr Harford had taken for his third wife, Elizabeth the daughter of Joyce's uncle Thomas Brydges of Old Colwall and the widow of John Dannett of Bosbury. His father, Doctor Harford, had married my wife's mother not long after the death of her husband, a union that had caused me considerable disquiet.

Although happy for her Cousin Elizabeth, my wife echoed my dislike of her step-father, even though he was held in high esteem in some quarters of Hereford. As well, young Bridstock's past led me to doubt his complete loyalty to the King, so I was loath to welcome another Harford as a kinsman.

Before his marriage to the widow Brydges, Doctor Harford had served on a number of local Assessment Commissions during Mr Cromwell's time in power, a matter that had not endeared him to many of his former Royalist friends, including that of my esteemed father. I suspected young Mr Harford to be an Exclusionist at heart, but he always greeted me cordially and was pleased to call me his cousin whenever we met.

I was greatly relieved when I learnt that he had decided against standing for Parliament again. My duty was now clear: I would put myself forward as a Representative of Hereford in his place. Mr Foley himself had ventured to suggest it. I had been fortunate to retain my estates, and so qualified as a landholder and although still in debt, I had not been declared bankrupt, largely thanks to my Lord Danby, who was still unhappily incarcerated in The Tower.

To my dismay, I learnt that my old rival, that untrustworthy man William Bowdler who had purloined my position as Receiver of Taxes only four years earlier, also intended standing. There being no love lost between us, I could never enter into any kind of partnership with him, even though he had been put forward by the Court and had convictions similar to mine. Mr Foley, now of Priors Court, gave out that he was offering himself as another candidate. My way was clear.

My wife Joyce still harboured a bitter resentment at having to sell her family's estate and the house where she and her sisters had grown up, but I told her that she should never forget that selling Priors Court to Mr Foley had been in the best interests of her husband and children. Its sale would help me ease my way to Westminster.

She reminded me again, that he had persuaded Sir Henry Lingen's widow Alice and his heirs to sell Stoke Edith to him, and when Captain Thomas Price was forced to sell Wistaston Court, Mr Foley bought it for a mere £3,650. I told her that being a woman, she had little understanding of financial niceties, and that besides, Mr Foley had a high reputation for rectitude and personal piety.

'According to John Birch! He is always extolling Paul Foley's wealth and bounty in works of charity, and besides, we know the man to be a Presbyterian. Is he not also an Exclusionist?' I ignored this remark, not wanting to give my wife the satisfaction of learning that her words rang uncomfortably true.

Paul Foley had indeed spoken in the last Parliament and asserted that he deemed it constitutional to alter the succession, even though he admitted that the outcome might come to blood. Yet what could I do, with the three of us, Mr Foley, Mr Bowdler and me, standing for the two positions?

If I joined with Mr Bowdler, which I would never contemplate, Mr Foley would likely lose. On the other hand, would Mr Foley join forces with Mr Bowdler and keep me out? Yet aligning myself with Mr Foley would mean successfully barring Mr Bowdler, forcing me to partner myself with an Exclusionist.

Nightly I searched my conscience and asked God for guidance. I naturally communicated my predicament to Secretary of State Sir Leoline Jenkins. He replied in part,

> *I offer it as my poor judgement that you should ... appeal & resign yourself to the gentlemen of the county that are most concerned & best affected for the king's service. ...This I say on a supposal that you intend to stand when a parliament is called, yet do not intend to withstand Mr F.* **Pray burn this**.

I neither burned the letter, nor stood against Mr F.

The general election was called and the Freemen cast their votes. To my great relief, when the numbers were counted, Mr Bowdler had failed to gain a sufficient total to be elected. Mr Foley and I had won the day.

Of course scurrilous stories immediately circulated. People whispered that Bowdler's defeat had only come about because of a secret coalition between Mr Foley and me. Mr Foley had violated a promise he had made to Lord Scudamore that he would solicit votes for himself only. Instead, he and I had made a tacit agreement to support each other. These innuendoes and gross untruths cut a swathe through Hereford for many days afterwards.

Of his alleged collusion with me, Mr Foley confessed to one of his accusers that when some friends had asked his advice as to whom they should give their second vote, he had only told them that he had such 'personal disobligations from Mr Bowdler' that they should give their vote to Mr Aubrey. Those were his exact words; advice that could hardly be called 'collusion'.

Such frankness and honesty could only be admired and I was proud to join him, Exclusionist or not, as the other Representative for Hereford, in company with the two Knights of the Shire, Lord Scudamore and Sir Edward Harley, even although the latter still held Puritanical views.

My brother Thomas had sent us regular reports from London of disturbances in the streets and periodic disruptions to civil order that stemmed from disputes about the Succession. On one occasion he found himself surrounded by a mob of youths and only escaped with life and limb by convincing them he wanted no Pope and no Catholic King.

He believed, as most others did, that the riots were fomented by Lord Shaftesbury. His Lordship had changed sides during the civil wars and had since contributed to the downfall of my Lord Danby who still had not been released from the Tower. Such a turncoat, a man who could serve both King and Cromwell, I distrusted above all others.

Thus, I was not surprised when His Majesty summoned all Members of this Parliament to meet, not at Westminster, but at Oxford.

28. Oxford

I was more than happy to return to that city of golden spires, the Royalist capital in the civil wars and where as a youth, I had spent so many valuable hours at Queen's College in study and discourse with like-minded men.

As befits the event, I had ordered new doublet and breeches to be made and bought a new wig. Joyce strenuously objected to the extravagance, but I reminded her that I was to be in the presence of His Majesty and that I should be attired appropriately. At the time, I was simply preparing for what would be for me, an auspicious occasion, one that I had so long yearned for; at last I would take my seat in Parliament together with Mr Paul Foley as Representatives of the city of Hereford.

Herbert and Brydges had begged to be allowed to come with me, so I generously acceded to their pleas, by having them attend me in lieu of a servant. They would be privileged to glimpse His Majesty and proud to see their father make his mark on a stage greater than that of Hereford.

We set out in good time and eventually met the undulating hills surrounding Oxford and approached that great city of learning, with growing excitement on my sons' part, and anxious anticipation on mine. Spring flowers were starting to appear, and Oxford had come alive with crowds and noise and confusion. Members and their entourages and servants jostled with pedlars and beggars and vendors of all description, anxious to sell their wares. Carriages and carts filled the streets and everywhere we looked were King's troops, armed with muskets at the ready to protect His Majesty against possible disturbances.

It pleased me greatly to be back there, to be among the other Representatives in this next important Parliament. I recognised many familiar faces from Herefordshire, most of whom deigned to bow in my direction in greeting. Then my heart turned over as I beheld Colonel John Birch, laughing in the midst of a group of followers. I forbore to recognise him, although he caught my eye and waved his plumed hat to me in an arrogant salutation.

It was necessary to explain to my sons that the man was only there because he had managed to get enough votes to represent Weobley as a result of his buying Roger Vaughen's family residence Garnstone. Scenes of young Roger flashed into my mind: him smiling and quaffing my wine, urging me to sign his surety, and his death and my subsequent financial nightmares.

Now the man to whom Roger had sold his wife's property, dared to greet me in the street. It was to him that I had had to pay the money I owed His Majesty – money that I did not have. I could only bury these recurring thoughts with an unaccustomed irritation. I bade my sons be silent – and refused to speak more.

We turned our horses into the High Street, which I reminded my sons was considered to be one of the noblest avenues in Europe, containing as it did, part of Queen's College, standing proud in its Grecian architecture, when we came upon an extraordinary sight. Four men, smiling and waving their hands, with troops of supporters came upon us in great state, wearing on their hats, silken ribbands on which were inscribed 'No Popery, No Slavery'.

Some of the bystanders and passers-by loudly cheered them on their way, which noise startled our horses. I caught the name 'Sir Robert Clayton'[1] from a voice in the crowd. Sure enough, I recognised his open and comely features marred only, in my eyes, by the somewhat fleshy apex of his protruding chin. Here was the man, risen from humble beginnings in Northamptonshire, and now Lord Mayor of London. He looked after the estates and fortunes of many in the Court and wielded great influence through his enormous wealth. According to Thomas, he was the richest man in the Kingdom – and an Exclusionist.

Herbert and Brydges questioned me incessantly as to the significance of the scene and the episode immediately cast a gloom. Sir Robert's distinguished air, his portly bearing and his sumptuous clothes all trumpeted his great fortune. His ostentatious gesture wearing the ribbands, presaged that Parliament could more than likely end like the previous ones. Powerful Exclusionists like him were come to make it so. I could only pray to God that my fears were unfounded and that they would say nothing to incur the wrath of the King.

As soon as we had found our way down the narrow winding alley off Holywell Street to the Turf Tavern, the only inn in which we could find a room, I made sure to visit my old alma mater. I could see that Brydges was consumed with admiration and I even noted a look on his face of envy, when he beheld the splendour of Queen's College. I allowed them both to say a prayer in its spacious and handsome chapel and visit the fine library where I had spent many hours in study. The old quadrangle still rang with young voices and I prayed to God that when Herbert attended its hallowed walls, he would come under the influence of men of learning and true devotion as I had done.

It was an opportune time to remind my eldest son of his many obligations that he would be obliged to meet the following year, when he began his study at Queen's College as I had arranged. Yes, he swore he would exert himself and yes, he would obey his tutor and yes, he would justify his presence at in that seat of learning and yes, he would daily pray for the soul of his grandfather in grateful thanks for the £100 that he left in his will for the purpose. He could not be there otherwise.

Two days later, at eight of the clock in the morning, I made my way to the History School where I joined the crowd of Members as were returned to serve in the King's Parliament. It proved to be a most unsuitable location, in fact so uncomfortable that it caused many of my fellow Members to complain bitterly, cursing the rioters in London who were responsible for us being here in Oxford instead of at Westminster. But we were here to serve His Majesty.

We were each of us in turn obliged to swear the Oaths of Allegiance and Supremacy, the Clerk of the Crown having the list of names which he read aloud in a sonorous tone and to my delight, it happened to be Henry Earl of Clarendon who administered the Oath to me. I knew he could not fail to remember the words of condolence I seized the opportunity of expressing to him, on the tenth anniversary of the death of his sister Anne, the late wife of His Excellency the Duke of York. He accepted my words with a smile and slight bow and immediately turned his attention to the next Member.

Soon the King commanded us to attend him immediately upstairs in the House of Peers. His Majesty gave us a pretty speech and then bade us return to our House and proceed with the choice of a Speaker.

These formalities, which included subscribing to the Act for the more effectual preserving the King's Person and Government by disabling Papists from sitting in either House of Parliament, took several days.

The following Thursday, it was resolved that a Committee of Elections and Privileges be appointed from a group of Members which included Mr Foley, Sir Robert Clayton – who had removed the ribbands from his attire - and that detestable man, Colonel Birch.

My name being among the dozens presented, and it being the first time I had served my King as a Member of his Parliament, I fully expected to be given an opportunity to speak. In anticipation of this important event, I had many sage words and loyal turns of phrase in my head ready to utter, with which to impress my hearers.

One of our number, Thomas Coningsby was given leave to make a maiden speech. A somewhat vain and impulsive young man, his Royalist family had lived at Hampton Court near Leominster for generations. The fact that the estate was now flourishing was largely thanks to the deep pockets of his father-in-law Captain Ferdinando Gorges. Mr Coningsby had voted for Exclusion in the last Parliament.

Now as well, I found his words not to my liking especially when he cast aspersions on my good friend Sir Leoline Jenkins. At the end of his speech, he bowed low to the Speaker of the House Mr Williams and sat down to subdued applause to which I could hardly bring myself to contribute.

The next day Sir Robert Clayton was among those named to make a Report to the House on Lord Danby's Impeachment. That reminded me that I should send His Lordship another collar of brawn and more cider, considering the fact that he was still in the Tower and that it was through his help that I was able to submit myself for election to this Parliament.

With so many members complaining of the discomfort we were experiencing in the History School, it was decided that a Committee be appointed to consider a more convenient place in Oxford for the sitting of the Commons in Parliament now assembled and to make a report to the House. Among the Members nominated were Mr Foley and Colonel Birch who seemed to be everywhere I turned – and Mr Lemuel Kingdon, the husband of Joyce's niece Theodosia.

The year before meeting him at the Oxford Parliament, Joyce had alerted me to some of the stories being bruited abroad concerning the young man. He had been returned for Kingston-upon-Hull in the earlier March 1679 Parliament, thanks to the influence of the Duke of Monmouth, the King's illegitimate son, with whom he came in close contact in his duties as Paymaster of the Forces. I could only applaud such good fortune being visited upon a kinsman. However, it seems that he had soon found himself in difficulties of a pecuniary nature and the

House had called him to account.

He had assured the Members that the whole of the £200,000 they had voted for paying off the recently raised forces had been properly disbursed. On the contrary, so the gossips said, the remaining forces had not been paid for ten months. As a result of this confusion, Sir Stephen Fox had been given back the position of Paymaster in place of Sir Henry Puckering and Mr Kingdon had been forced to give up his post as Deputy and to quit his official residence in Whitehall.

I found the story of his financial misdemeanour difficult to believe, but also disturbing for the good name of my wife's family were other stories circulating in Oxford at the time, that his wife Theodosia was seeing a great deal more of Sir Robert Holmes[2], the Governor of the Isle of Wight than was entirely proper. The pair were often observed together in London and it was through the influence of Sir Robert, the Kingdon's neighbour in Whitehall, that Theodosia's husband had been returned as Member for Yarmouth in this Parliament.

They said that Mr and Mrs Kingdon were frequent guests at Sir Robert's Isle of Wight mansion and my wife heard tell that Sir Robert was so much under young Theodosia's spell, that he would do her bidding in anything.

As we dispersed after that first day, to my surprise, I saw the young gentleman himself striding purposefully through the crowd towards me. A tall man with a commanding presence, I knew Mr Kingdon instilled fear into all who crossed him, but could crease his face into a broad smile when the mood took him. I was flattered that he always greeted me as if I were his long-long brother.

This day, he addressed me warmly and I immediately seized the opportunity to enquire after the health of his good wife Theodosia, as Joyce had bidden me. He responded to the question in a non-committal manner, and seemed rather more concerned with confiding in me his recent financial 'difficulties', as he called them. He drew me aside.

'You see before you a wronged man! I swear to God that the whole of the £200,000 we voted in the House for paying off the forces two years ago was properly disbursed – I myself inspected the accounts - but my enemies, of which I have many, took the opportunity to deprive me of the office of Deputy Paymaster. And for that, I almost faced ruin!'

Hearing his words, I could only sympathise, having faced a similar, but admittedly less dire situation myself. But he continued before I found the words to commiserate:

'However, thanks to the auspices of my good friends, Sir Robert Holmes in particular, you seem me here, as a Member for Yarmouth. Furthermore, I have another speculations – plans - in mind, one in particular that involves your good wife's kinsman William Brydges. I confidently expect one in particular to reap us rich returns! I'll say no more now, but – my duty to your good lady – and we shall speak again.' He paused. 'I tell you all this because I esteem you, Mr Aubrey, *as a kinsmen I respect and in whom I can confide'*. Those were the very words he used.

With that, he bowed his adieux and turned on his heel. The prospect of our family being involved in Mr Kingdon's future plans, and their rewards, excited my curiosity and I resolved to learn more about them at the earliest opportunity.

The next day, that which I had dreaded most, came to pass. After much debate, some of it acrimonious, it was resolved that a Bill be brought in, to exclude James, Duke of York and all Popish Successors from inheriting the Imperial Crowns of England and Ireland, and the Dominions and Territories thereunto belonging. Among the Members appointed to prepare and draw up the Bill were Mr Foley and Sir Robert Clayton.

It was the third attempt in almost as many years to exclude the Duke of York from the throne. As to be expected, the King refused to accept the Bill and proclaimed Parliament dissolved.

We had been there less than a week.

---

1. Sir Robert Clayton (1629-1707) M.P. and financier. He became apprenticed to his uncle, a London scrivener. He and another apprentice, John Morris, established the bank, Clayton and Morris. (see n115). He entered politics, was knighted in 1671, and elected Lord Mayor of London. He built a considerable fortune which, in 1697, enabled him to lend the King £30,000 to pay off the troops. He built a sumptuous estate at Marden Park and not having a son and heir, left his wealth to a nephew.

2. Sir Robert Holmes (1622-1692) Royalist Naval Captain. After a successful naval career, the highlight of which was his destruction of a large part of the Dutch merchant marine, he retired to the Isle of Wight where he became Governor. Adventurous and unscrupulous, he had an illegitimate daughter Mary, who eventually married his nephew. Rumours abounded that her mother was Theodosia Kingdon as gossips believed them to be having an affair.

29. Consequences

Let no man deny that fate plays a part in the affairs of men, for my visit to Oxford later proved to be a turning point in the destiny of our family. Immediately we left the chamber, disgruntled Members, mostly Exclusionists, gathered in groups to voice their anger and frustration. To me there was no question: His Majesty had done the only right and proper thing. The movement to exclude the rightful heir to the throne was growing apace and it had to be stopped and rooted out once and for all.

As the crowd dispersed, I searched for my fellow Member Mr Foley, but in vain. Then I heard a rumour that he was attending a meeting at Lord Scudamore's lodgings with other 'like minded' Members. The possible consequences of this gathering worried me greatly, especially when the names of the others present were revealed.

That dangerous little man Lord Shaftesbury was foremost among them and we all knew how much he supported Exclusion. People whispered another name, that of Captain Ferdinando Gorges who claimed kinship with His Lordship and who had recently bought the manor of Eye in Herefordshire. I believed him to have Puritan leanings. Captain Gorges was Mr Coningsby's father-in-law and I suspected the young man owed him a debt of gratitude for bringing his family estates into some kind of financial order.

Could young Lord Scudamore be seduced by the likes of such men? His fellow Knight of the Shire, Sir Edward Harley with his Puritan background? Mr Foley, knowing him to be an Exclusionist? The little turncoat Lord Shaftesbury, who had once been a member of Cromwell's Council of State? Even though the King had graciously pardoned him, such a man could never be trusted – particularly so when he had been largely instrumental in having my Lord Danby sent to the Tower.

Rumour had it that during the meeting at Lord Scudamore's lodgings, there was talk of armed resistance, bearing out Mr Foley's dire warning to the previous Parliament that altering the succession could result in blood. Scenes that I had witnessed as a child, when kin fought kin, came to my mind. Could such a calamity as excluding the rightful heir to the throne of England in fact come to pass and worse still, end in death and destruction?

Yet in spite of my dark foreboding and the likelihood of his being influenced by such obdurate men, I found it difficult to believe any ill of young Lord Scudamore, coming as he did from such a distinguished family and he being a distant kinsman. I could only wait and pray for a rightful outcome.

***

Before returning to Hereford, I took the opportunity of showing my sons the Botanic Gardens near Magdalen Bridge where I had spent so many happy hours in my youth. We had just crossed the bridge when we chanced to see Mr Foley walking towards us, deep in conversation with another man. As they drew nearer, I saw him to be Sir Robert Clayton, the influential Exclusionist. Behind them, ambled a retinue of young blades, chattering and laughing.

Naturally we stopped and bowed our greetings and Mr Foley did us the honour of introducing us. A thousand contradictory thoughts rushed through my mind, but after the usual pleasantries were exchanged, I made bold to say,

'Sir Robert, you do my family a great honour.' He looked puzzled. 'My young brother Thomas is in your employ - I trust he does justice to the position in which you have been good enough place him.'

Sir Robert's face lit up in comprehension. 'Ah yes, the youngest son! Indeed he does Mr Aubrey! Although I hear', he hesitated and coughed delicately, 'that young Mr Aubrey likes to spend his spare moments – of which he has few – at the Mermaid Tavern playing at dice – and sometimes even wins!'

The group of sycophants shuffling behind them, for that is what I suspected them to be, joined in the merriment hearing the great man's laughter and then idled away as the conversation continued. At that, Sir Robert engaged young Herbert in animated conversation, to the exclusion of the rest of us. I only hoped that Herbert's ready smiles and quick responses to the great man's words would not be considered too familiar.

At the same time, Mr Foley asked Brydges questions that youths of that age can bring themselves to answer without hesitation: What is the name of his favourite horse? How strict are his masters at school? Would he like to visit Priors Court and see where his mother once lived?

I was listening to all this with a degree of satisfaction, when Sir

Robert turned to me as if struck by a sudden thought, 'Mr Aubrey, I should like this young man to have your permission to visit me at Marden Park – when of course his studies permit.' I could only bow and acquiesce to such a gracious and unexpected invitation which did my son and heir so much honour.

Exclusionist he may be, but Thomas had told me that his huge land owning gave him rents of nearly £4,000 a year and his interest on loans almost as much. More to the point, the great man had no heir, an only son having died in infancy.

We bade our adieux and parted, not before Sir Robert reminding us that he anticipated my son's visit with the greatest of pleasure. Thus fate intervened in young Herbert's life with consequences none of us foresaw.

We made our way back to Herefordshire, my son exultant with pleasure and I with exceeding confused feelings. Brydges demanded to know why Herbert had been so honoured? The latter would have taken off for Sir Robert's country estate the next day, had it been possible. I liked it not that he could come under the influence an Exclusionist, wealthy as he was. Yet, Sir Robert had no heir – I stifled that train of thought at once.

Not long after our return to Herefordshire, more immediate matters claimed our attention when Lord Scudamore found himself a victim of a sequence of scandalous events.

Several months after the Oxford Parliament had been dissolved, Lord Scudamore felt it his duty to summon me to his seat, Holme Lacey, and of course most of those other former Members from Herefordshire who were also disturbed by the course of events and the turmoil in the country.

Among My Lord's guests at the gathering, I immediately noticed Mr Coningsby of Hampton Court. He and a small group of admirers greeted my presence coolly, bowing with only the minimum of courtesy while the young man continued to regale them with the success of his maiden speech at Oxford. Mrs Coningsby who was seated nearby, had doubtless heard his words many times repeated and revealed her boredom and ill manners by constantly tapping her fan to gain attention to herself. I was pleased my own wife was not present to witness such unseemly feminine behaviour.

Mr Coningsby liked to boast that between the time of Queen

Elizabeth and the Troubles, his ancestors had represented the county seven times, which story always amazed his listeners. But I knew for a fact that when his grandfather Fitzwilliam Coningsby stood for Leominster in 1661, he was denied the poll, being at the time in prison for debt.

Mr Coningsby's father had mortgaged the estate and his mother at one time was a prisoner in the King's Bench. Furthermore, the young man's marriage to Captain Gorges' daughter Barbara was said to have been initiated by the Barbados merchant without the consent of either of Mr Coningsby's parents. Such facts did nothing to humble the young man's arrogance.

Lord and Lady Scudamore had long been on intimate terms with Mr and Mrs Coningsby, whom I quickly perceived at this meeting were being afforded special attention. I soon learned that they were enjoying the delights of Holme Lacey as his Lordship's guests.

Lady Scudamore ensured that our needs were quickly attended to in the way of refreshments and I noted that her eyes were very often drawn to those of Mr Coningsby, who sometimes found it difficult to follow the thread of our often lively discussions when our hostess was in the room.

After many speeches and entreaties, Lord Scudamore allayed our fears that he had been tempted to join the Exclusionist camp. He assured us all that he would never be part of any unconstitutional measure to alter the succession. We then urged His Lordship to stand again as Knight of the Shire in the next election, on condition that he would undertake not to join with anyone of a contrary persuasion. His response could have been firmer and more convincing, but we had needs be satisfied for the time being and the meeting ended amicably enough.

The following month, the Coningsbys returned Lord and Lady Scudamore's hospitality by issuing them an invitation to their seat, Hampton Court. My wife reported the sequence of events to me as she heard them, the shameful incidents that occurred during their visit. Loath as I was to listen to gossip, nevertheless as the situation had political ramifications, I attended to what she had to say. Tom, the brother of our kitchen maid Ellen, worked as a groom at Hampton Court and so the story came to Clehonger Manor and then to my wife who reported it, as she felt duty bound, to me.

'One day during Lord and Lady Scudamore's stay at Hampton Court,

His Lordship was sitting in the great parlour alone with Mrs Coningsby. A maid, who had been summoned to do an errand for her mistress, entered the room and saw His Lordship stifle a yawn. He then rose to his feet and begged his hostess to guide him through the maze as it was so well known throughout the county and it being the case, t'was a pity he would be one of the few people never to have been through it.'

I had never been through it, neither, but the thought of being there only in the company of Mrs Coningsby hardly appealed to me and I told my wife to get to the crux of the report.

'Not showing much enthusiasm, Mrs Coningsby told the maid to fetch her a cloak and off they set. Tom saw them emerge from the maze some time later, Mrs Coningsby dragging her feet and hardly keeping up with Lord Scudamore. Tom overheard his Lordship beg her to show him the tower now as he wanted to view the sunken garden from that vantage point.'

My wife paused here to smile at the scene as she had heard it described, but I reminded her how easily one's servants could know our personal affairs and that she should never forget it.

'When they returned inside at last, Mrs Coningsby demanded of the servants, the whereabouts of her husband. She begged leave of Lord Scudamore and went searching for him. According to her maid who witnessed the scene, Mrs Coningsby heard laughter issuing from behind the door of her husband's chamber. She looked through the keyhole and screamed.

Mr Coningsby was dallying with Lady Scudamore. She burst in on the couple and accused them both, at the top of her voice, of the most cruel and wicked deceit. The wronged wife thereupon swooned and had to be brought round with a liberal application of smelling salts.'

Such was the report from Hampton Court, which I could well believe, knowing that Mrs Coningsby possessed an intemperate and fiery nature at the best of times, but worse was to come. Some little time later, and not content with the revelation and consequences of that disgraceful scene, Mr Coningsby and Lady Scudamore took the first opportunity to run away together.

At that, My Lord ordered two of his trusted servants to follow the guilty pair and to bring them back at pistol point. It was not long before the two were returned to scenes of vituperation on the part of Mrs

Coningsby, and cool disdain on the part of His Lordship. The humiliation of his wife's guilty flight removed him from politics for the time being, but with true Christian generosity, Lord Scudamore forgave his wife and took her back.

Joyce continued to take what I considered to be a prurient interest in the sordid affair. She reported to me that Mrs Coningsby's father Captain Gorges had played a key role in the reconciliation. I remembered Mr Coningsby's telling me in Oxford that his father-in-law had urged him to write to him all the proceedings of Parliament. Even at the time, I feared that the 'King of the Blacks', as he was known because of the great wealth he had acquired from the slave trade, exerted an unhealthy influence on his son-in-law. Doubtless he wanted it to continue.

So the couples renewed their conjugal obligations as they had vowed to God to obey, although, again according to my wife, Mrs Coningsby told her friends that she would never forgive her husband's infidelity and swore to remind him of it at every opportunity.

30. Exclusion

The question of Exclusion still dominated our minds. To my consternation I now heard that Mr Coningsby was holding clandestine meetings of Exclusionists at his home at Hampton Court, with or without the presence of his wife, nobody could tell. We knew that many in Herefordshire were actively working against the union of the King's supporters and that prominent among them was that immoral man, Colonel John Birch, a frequent guest at Hampton Court.

By now I had learnt the nature of the scheme that Mr Kingdon had hinted at when we met at Oxford. He had formed a syndicate, made up of my wife's cousin Mr Brydges and a Mr Trant whom they said 'had Irish connections'. The Treasury had allowed the Hearth Tax surplus to be farmed out to a Mr Genew who in turn, for a consideration so it was said, promptly – and surreptitiously - made it over to young Lemuel's syndicate. Now there should have been money a-plenty, but already the scheme was running into difficulties and he and his partners owed the Crown several thousand pounds. I gave myself the satisfaction of being thankful that he had not included me in that plan as I had hoped he might.

Meanwhile, up and down the country, Royalists were obtaining a Loyal Address from local supporters, thus providing indisputable evidence of their devotion to the King and his brother the Duke of York. In Hereford, Colonel Birch was doing everything in his power to hinder and obstruct these upright people. He intimidated the local populace and threatened good and worthy subjects with ruin and starvation if they did not do his bidding. I made no bones about relating all this to Sir Leoline and finished my letter by saying of this immoral degenerate, 'if he be anything, I think him an Athiest.'

My friend Sir John Morgan and Sir John Hoskyns, a fellow Commissioner for Assessment, both presented Loyal Addresses in spite of much opposition. I am happy to say that nothing stinted my efforts in this regard as well, even although Exclusionists, at the instigation of Colonel Birch, hindered us at every opportunity.

At the summer Assizes, I took it upon myself to deliver the charge to the Grand Jury. It took me some time to persuade them to demonstrate their loyalty to His Majesty, for there were men present who vehemently opposed me. But I knew that right was on my side and I took the opportunity to articulate those turns of phrase that I had been unable to express a few months earlier in the Oxford Parliament, as it now came to be known. Without succumbing to the sin of Pride, success attained my efforts and my rhetoric had the desired effect.

I finally succeeded in obtaining a Loyal Address from them, approving the dissolution of Parliament and thus ensuring their support for the King. I sent it poste haste to Sir Leoline, who, in his meticulous way, as always, responded, albeit briefly.

23 July 1681 Whitehall. Secretary Jenkins to Herbert Aubrey. Last Thursday at Hampton Court I presented to HM the address of the grand jury of Herefords at their quarter sessions. He commanded me to return them his hearty thanks & to assure them that his full purpose was by the grace of God to stand by the church & govern by the law. You will please communicate this to your friends.

I was more than happy to obey His Majesty's Royal command.

I continued to report to Secretary of State Jenkins on local affairs, particularly the loyalty or otherwise of political contenders and religious dissenters like the Quakers who were pestering me to take a 'test and sign a certificate'. All these matters I communicated in detail to Sir Leoline Jenkins. In the case of the Quakers, I wrote that I had

'promised to lay the whole affair before you and to act as HM directs. Post script. Sir John Morgan is with me and drinks your health.'

I had few friends in whom I could confide, but Sir John Morgan kept my trust and understood me. A tall man with an upright bearing, he had embraced a military career and having seen service with Prince William of Orange. He thus knew the values of loyalty and discipline, and although about twenty years younger than I, we had much in common. We were both Members of Parliament, both Herefordshire men, and our families were Royalist to the core. Like many other such believers, both of us were severely put to the test when it later came to choosing between King and Catholicism.

I came to rely on Sir John's friendship, while the King's enemies – led, I'm convinced by Colonel John Birch - spread untruths and malicious gossip about me. I spent much time with pen in hand writing to Sir Leoline, who always answered my letters. When I complained to him in one of them, of being '*disrespected*', as I put it. He responded sympathetically, writing that he was sorry to hear it and added '*if it lay in my power to vindicate you, I would do it most readily.*' Such words of comfort sustained me during these difficult times.

I only knew that I was destined to serve my King, and this is what I would soon do, once again, but this time, in the nation's capital – but never, I vowed, would I stand again with Mr Foley. To Lord Scudamore's displeasure, and of course mine, he now openly associated with Colonel Birch and Sir Edward Harley and other ill-affected persons, all of which I made sure to report to Sir Leoline.

In one of his numerous replies, he indicated that my Lord Rochester was considering me for the office of Collector of Excise and I confidently expected a sympathetic consideration.

After I succeeded in obtaining the Loyal Address, I continued to involve myself in local government, firstly as an Alderman and then as one of the thirteen Deputy Lord Lieutenants of the county, among the others being my old friends Herbert Westfaling, Humphrey Cornewall and Sir Henry Croft. I considered myself more than ably suited to hold that important office, and I was often obliged to concern myself with events of a somewhat parochial, but nevertheless instructional nature.

One such episode, in the early winter months of 1683 that many people remembered long afterwards, involved the local shoemaker, Edward Dyer. I knew him to be a God-fearing man, a Royalist and one who ever demanded high standards of his son and heir whom he confidently expected would succeed him in his trade. Gradually, he came to the realisation that young Master Dyer was spending his time – and his pennies - rather more than was consistent with his means, at the Boothall Inn.

Dyer leapt to the only possible conclusion. His son was robbing him to pay for his moral degeneration. He went to the Mayor forthwith and demanded he take out a warrant against his son. The Mayor listened sympathetically to the sorry tale and gave the necessary instructions.

That very same evening, Sergeant John Jones happened to find young Dyer drinking at the Boothall Inn and told him a warrant had been taken out against him. Hoping to keep the peace, Sergeant Jones assured the miscreant that if he but came quietly, he was sure the Mayor would reconcile him with his father.

Hardly had the words been uttered when the young man, taken with drink and now filled with rage, struck at the Sergeant. He swore he would kill any man who dared try to arrest him. The other drinkers watched with interest as a fight ensued and there was even talk of bets being taken. But the young man got the better of the older and somewhat portly arm of the law. While Sergeant Jones was recovering from the blows he had received in the uneven match, the innkeeper and his wife and children spirited young Dyer away.

Soon after this confrontation in the Inn, Sergeant Jones, bloody but unbowed, happened to meet the Mayor and his Lady Wife walking down the street on their way home. He was relating the sequence of events and explaining his unseemly appearance, when the Mayor spied young Dyer in the distance. Sergeant Jones was ordered to apprehend the villain and arrest him on the spot.

In the interim Dyer had rewarded himself with a few more pints of ale and had even armed himself with a cudgel. As he approached, the Sergeant met the same reaction as before. Dyer raised the cudgel and responded with very base and threatening language. This so infuriated the Mayor, that his wife should find herself in the vicinity of such a turn of events and be the audience of such abusive language, that he bought into the fray and another round ensued.

A great rabble gathered. Dyer attacked the Mayor with his cudgel and had him down on one knee, but the Mayor seized the fellow and in the ensuring fracas, found himself minus his hat and periwig and with his best lace-edged silk neck scarf torn.

The Mayor's lady wife also lost her hat, and was furious and embarrassed at being the subject of derision of the growing crowd of onlookers, who seemed rather to come to look on with amusement or even rescue the fellow, than to assist the Mayor.

Finally, help arrived and the prisoner was captured and put on bail for £200. He was to be censured in public to deter others from like affronts to the government in the person of His Majesty's lieutenant.

I took up my pen on the fifth day of February 1683 and reported the affray to Sir Leoline Jenkins. Commenting on those who actively aided Dyer and who failed to help the Mayor, I expressed the confident opinion that some would surely be disfranchised, ending my account,

> *I doubt not but the city will be very quiet, when this crime has passed all the forms of law and justice, and our town bullies will be afraid to venture on outrages so like rebellion. We are all here in perfect peace, full of love of our good King and the government as by law established... The Mayor has behaved in this with great resolution.*

To my sons, I reiterated this account, in the hope that they would heed the lesson of how, by his unnatural actions, a disaffected son brought shame and distress to his father, his family and even some of the townsfolk. I advised them to ponder on the dire consequences that ensued from such behaviour and to learn well from it, especially young Herbert who was about to set out for London from whence he would travel with Sir Robert Clayton's entourage to his country seat of Marden. When I learned of the money he had spent on its construction, I could not but wonder why young Herbert had been so honoured, and not I.

For weeks he could talk of nothing else, while Brydges constantly bemoaned the fact that he had been born the second son and was doomed to a life of misery on that account. In my heart I could only sympathise with him, as I remembered with shame my feelings of hatred towards Samuel and then my remorse at his death.

Young Herbert had grown into a strong, self-possessed young man polished and assured after his years at Queen's College which learning had been paid for by the generosity of his maternal grandfather's will. He liked to have his own way, often at the expense of others and particularly his siblings.

He disappointed me in several other important respects: he showed little or no interest in the cause which was then consuming me, namely the Succession. Nor did he express other than merely outward shows of devotion to the Established Church which institution had sustained me and nurtured my faith these many years.

Any discussion with him touching on these matters somehow always resulted in ill temper and raised voices. Unfortunately his mother indulged him in everything and he was now too big for me to take a strap to him to show him the error of his ways.

On the other hand, to my great satisfaction, young Reginald, although only fourteen years old, was begging me to find the money to send him to Balliol, my father's old Oxford College on which he had set his heart, in order to study for the Church. I was determined to find the means in order to make this possible for him.

I had been made Collector of the local Hearth Tax or as the common people referred to it, 'chimney money'. Many still objected to the tax even though it had been levied since 1662. They complained at not only having to pay two shillings per hearth every half year, but having the Collectors enter and search their dwellings.

I was honoured to be given this responsibility but this time, experience dictated that I take even more care with the money entrusted to me. Joyce made her views known, as she was wont to do, and unasked, on the possible effect on my health that this addition burden would incur. I know she spoke out of concern for the well being of her Lord and Master – but I was forced to remind her men in my position were born to shoulder such duties for their King and country, however onerous.

As Receiver General of the Hearth Tax, I chose the Collectors of the same with great care, rejecting those whose past experience cast the slightest doubt on their honesty and integrity. I took great pains to give them all the necessary instructions, reminding them yet again to take due care and diligence in their undertaking. I gave them their books and sent them forth to count the hearths and record the names of the inhabitants and receive and note the money. A simple enough task, one would think. Nevertheless, difficulties arose and problems mounted, not of my making.

One Collector had not cleared his books from the previous half year, in spite of his many assurances to the contrary. Worse still, he had not paid in any of the money he had collected. For this, and other discrepancies, I was now responsible.

Another had failed to record the fact that several buildings were being erected. Yet another caused me great pains when the inhabitants of a particular dwelling which had two chimneys, claimed exemption on the grounds of poverty. The Collector demanded to know the name of the landlord, because it was he who now had to pay the tax. They could not, or would not reveal the landlord's name. I could not believe such a devious tale.

Other landlords proved equally elusive. One such remained in arrears for months, refusing to pay because he claimed his tenants of the two dwellings into which his house had been divided should pay and did not qualify to be exempted on the grounds of poverty. One claimed that he had already paid, but that it had not been duly recorded.

As a result of all these disagreements and confusions, my books fell into great disorder and consequently the accounts became extremely confused. Many hands had crossed out names in the books and in the columns, entries of monies had been altered, with the unfortunate result that it gave the whole a most suspicious look. In summation, these predicaments and the knowledge that my good name was at stake, affected my health to the point that I was forced to take to my bed sometimes for days at a time.

Then to my dismay, a rumour came to me that one Richard Cox would soon take my place as Receiver General of Hearth Money. I immediately wrote to Sir Leoline Jenkins begging him to ascertain if the Commissioners of Excise were indeed replacing me. I waited in vain for a reply to my letter and I was soon to learn that the Secretary of State was facing his own difficulties.

31. London

My wife insisted on keeping herself informed of stories circulating in London about her niece Theodosia, most of which came her way from the pen of her cousin William Brydges, a business associate of Mr Kingdon. One day she found me in my study, she with a letter in her hand and a look of disdain on her face.

'William tells me that Sir Robert Holmes has conveyed the property of New Park in the New Forest to Theodosia's husband, with reversions to the wench herself! 'Tis passing strange, do you not think so Mr Aubrey?' I remained silent, knowing that my informant would give her own views before attending to mine.

'Why would the great man do that pray, if it were not some sort of a recompense for – certain services rendered? All the world knows that Sir Robert has a daughter, born out of wedlock whom he has acknowledged and named Mary.' She paused, 'Nobody knows for certain who the mother is, but for years now, people have spoken his name in the same breath as that of Mrs Kingdon!

'This means, with Mr Kingdon being in poor health, as they say he is, that thanks to Sir Robert, on the possible early demise of her husband, she will inherit the property in the New Forest! What think you of that!'

She did not wait for my considered reply, but continued, 'And further, Mr Kingdon's supposed ill-health does not prevent him from being on *more* than friendly terms with Mrs Behn!'

I already knew that Mrs Behn had dedicated one of her plays 'The Feign'd Courtesans' to the King's current favourite, Mistress Nell Gwynn. 'Doubtless to find favour with His Majesty,' was my wife's comment, even although I had advised her to ignore idle gossip, especially on such a frivolous subject as Alphra Behen – a woman, a playwright, and a poet, all occupations I considered entirely unsuitable for a woman.

But ignoring my direction, my wife learnt more, and reported to me that Mrs Behn had dedicated her work, 'Love Letters Between a Nobleman and His Sister' to Theodosia's husband. Sure enough, Thomas confirmed that copies of her work, one surely of doubtful morality, were at a premium and its publication was the talk of London. I knew not what to make of Mr Kingdon's association with such a woman. Joyce, on the other hand, still deemed the character of her niece's husband to warrant suspicion, refusing to believe my own considered opinion of a man who had the ear of the Duke of Monmouth and other men of influence.

As for Mrs Kingdon, she was still keeping gossips busy by being seen frequently in the company of Sir Robert Holmes in London, at the theatre and visiting Foxhall and Hyde Park. She even remained in England 'to care for her children', as Joyce ironically described it, when Mr Kingdon left for Ireland to take up his appointment to the Irish Revenue Commission.

Although still in debt as a result of his dealings with the Pay Office, his appointment, thanks to some of his influential friends like Lord Ranelagh and Sir Edward Seymour, he was able to take it up with a salary of £1,000 per annum. Such a position - and the remuneration - I thought would suit my talents admirably.

Mrs Kingdon was said to be distraught at the thought of leaving all her dear friends and swore she would never abide living among savages, but would remain in London. 'Your Mr Kingdon was forced to borrow over £6,000 from his mother before leaving the country', my wife informed me, 'no doubt to avoid his creditors!'

She failed to understand that men who deal in money have of necessity to take risks. To me, the fact that his widowed mother could so easily give him such a sum, only proved that his father had accumulated much wealth from his position as Paymaster as well as his involvement in syndicates with men of power. These were influential men whom his son now called his friends.

Some time later, stories drifted back to England that Mr Kingdon was dominating the Board with an imperious, governing temper and that his health was failing – doubtless as a result of all his 'dubious financial dealings' was how my wife reacted to this intelligence. She could only thank God that her dear sister Margaret was not alive to see the disreputable state into which her daughter Theodosia and her husband had fallen. By now my wife was giving more and more voice to such irrational thoughts, which hysteria I considered it wise to ignore, for I too, was now an associate of Mr Kingdon.

Some time before, I was flattered when the young man eventually persuaded me to join him in a number of enterprises. The most important of them involved some 500 acres in part of the Manor of Park on the edge of the town of Ledbury. I grasped the opportunity of investing in the syndicate he had formed, leasing the land and tenements out for the rents there at a handsome profit.

After a lengthy and detailed discussion, I was convinced by his assurance that it would yield me a handsome return for my money, which of course would be of little difficulty to borrow. Mr Kingdon allayed my concerns by repeatedly assuring me of the worth of my investment. I was thus confident of its providing me with a good return. I had only needs bide my time.

The year 1683 brought the coldest winter in living memory. We heard stories of the Thames being frozen over from London Bridge to Blackfriars Bridge and the river being put to use as a vast fairground. Many poor souls in our county died from the bitter cold that in spite of all the fires we could burn, permeated every nook and cranny of Clehonger Manor.

My added duties and responsibilities, which now included the Captaincy of our Militia Horse, kept me ever more busy with my correspondence with Whitehall, being happy in the knowledge that my loyalty and local knowledge was of value to the Government. I was therefore particularly saddened when I heard that a man I had come to call a friend and confidante, Sir Leoline Jenkins had resigned the Great Seal.

No matter how many other affairs of State occupied his time, he never failed to answer the many epistles that I penned to him over the years. He paid for his earnest devotion to duty with a series of ailments that weakened his health, which forced him to retire to his house at Hammersmith. He lived only two years on, to enjoy the bounty of the £5,000 he took with him.

From time to time, I had occasion to visit my brother Thomas in London. Thomas had been able to keep me *au fait* with political gossip by becoming a member of the Green Ribbon Club, which met regularly at the King's Head Tavern in Chancery Lane. My first response was one of anger when he acquainted me with the names of some of its members, many of whom were Dissenters and Exclusionists. Worse, the association had been formed some years before by the Earl of Shaftesbury who by now, to the relief of many, had gone to his Maker.

However, after thoughtful consideration, I deemed my brother's association with the Club and its members could be of value, if he could keep me informed of important events he knew would be of interest to me. He wanted to 'hold his finger on the political pulse', was how he described his association with the Club. Thomas swore to me that he would never support the exclusion of the Duke of York to the throne of England and true to his word, he wrote to me regularly.

He had also enlarged his circle of friends and acquaintances as a result of his position with Clayton and Morris. Mr Morris was now dead and the bulk of his capital and interest on his own investments had gone to Sir Robert, whom Thomas assured me was devastated at the loss of his old friend and colleague.

The fact that Sir Robert had moved to introduce the Exclusion Bill at Oxford did him no favour with some of London's business interests, which gave me a degree of satisfaction. Thomas still collected rents, wrote out and signed agreements when directed, made himself agreeable to recalcitrant customers, and seemed sanguine about his future.

One visit to London was in order to learn from his own lips, everything he could find out about the family of Judith Cole and their relationship with the Honourable Charles Bertie, Lady Danby's brother. My son and heir could talk of nothing but of Northamptonshire where he had visited and the families with which he was now intimate, thanks to Sir Robert Clayton. He had set his mind on marrying the daughter of the man – the Presbyterian – whose acquaintance I had made at Sir Joseph Williamson's *soirée*.

Thomas welcomed me to his lodgings and over a meal at a nearby eating-house, which I was generous enough to buy for us for only eight shillings. He came straight to the point. 'The little I have gleaned, has come from the lips of Sir Robert's brother, Mr Peter Clayton.

'The girl's mother was previously married to Peter Tryon of Harringworth in Northamptonshire, by whom she had several children, one of whom, Mary, married the Honourable Charles Bertie, whom I believe you have met.

'On Mr Tryon's death, Mrs Tryon married Thomas Cole of Lyss in Hampshire. As you know, he represented Hampshire back in 1656 and 1660 and held several local offices during Cromwell's time.' Being reminded of the man's Presbyterian sympathies almost spoilt my enjoyment the venison, strong as it smelt on the plate. Thomas commanded another jug of ale.

'Mr Cole had previously been married to Sir Stephen Harvey's daughter Elizabeth in Warwickshire and when he married the Widow Tryon, they lived in Northamptonshire. During his lifetime Mr Cole himself and members of the Tryon family have long been intimate with Sir Robert Clayton and his family.' Thomas paused to allow me to digest this intelligence together with the strong meat in front of me.

'I believe Mr Cole's son Charles Cole now resides at Lyss. And another item, brother,' Thomas paused for effect. 'I know for a fact that Mr Cole's mother was Mary Waller, a cousin of that Sir William Waller whose exploits in Hereford during the Troubles we both remember, do we not?' I near choked on my food and only retained my composure after quaffing another glass of ale. Thomas waited and with what I observed as a sly smile added, 'Money or no, they are all Whigs and tarred with the same Puritan brush!'

We walked slowly back to Thomas's cramped and uncomfortable lodgings. That night I lay awake for a long time, listening to the watchman calling out the hours as my resolve strengthened.

While I had breath in my body, I determined never to countenance the marriage of my son and heir to the daughter of Thomas Cole and a cousin of that Parliamentary general who had hastened the death of my dear grandfather.

32. Interludes

From time to time, I remembered my Lord Danby still incarcerated in the Tower. So on that visit to Thomas, I made sure to call on him which I could now do without fear of reprisals or confrontation by the guards. Instead, I was ushered into his quarters where he and his Lady greeted me most kindly. His Lordship repeated many times over, his thanks for my letters and for my not forgetting to send him the occasional collar of brawn and bottles of cider. I found him more pale in visage and somewhat stooped and in spite of the fact we were the same age, I thought that he looked considerably older than I.

After our greetings and my enquiries as to his health, his Lady immediately took command of the conversation. She seemed to relish the presence of a new listener to their tales of woe – of which, apart from His Lordship's incarceration, she had many to report.

Firstly, she informed me, the husband of their dear darling daughter Bridget (named of course for her mother) had died, cruelly taken from the world at the age of four and twenty. I knew that the Earl of Plymouth was one of His Majesty's natural sons and had wed my Lordship's daughter Bridget only the year after the marriage of Prince William of Orange to the Prince of Wales' daughter Mary.

'So young! So handsome!' cried my Lady, tears coming to her eyes. 'We all loved him dearly, a true son of His Majesty's! Don Carlos, we used to call him! And to die just like that, during the siege of Tangiers by the infidels! In a foreign land!'

Before I could express my condolences at such a sad loss, she continued: 'And Elizabeth! Our dear Edward's wife! Taken from us in childbed! At the age of one and twenty!' At that, My Lordship patted her hand and bade her be calm, reminding her that the ways of God were wondrous strange.

I sought to change the subject and arrive at a happier one by mentioning Lord Shaftesbury who had also just died, he having been one of the main instruments for having My Lordship sent to the Tower. But rather than placate my Lady, no sooner had the words 'Shaftesbury' left my mouth, when she leapt to her feet again and began:

'Yes! He was sent here and rightly so! He claimed he was ill with the ague and the Governor permitted him to take the air in his coach with his Lady and servants! But never did *my* Lord receive such an indulgence! And more!' she drew breath, 'when the heat of August became so relentless, the Governor moved him to cooler rooms! I hope he is now roasting and rotting in a hotter hell than this!' At that, she sat and fanned herself as if to prove her point.

I gently enquired of her Ladyship the health of her brother, Mr Bertie. This brought on yet another burst of words. 'Charles has been a pillar of strength! But Peregrine! How could he, our dear son, take it upon himself to marry Miss Hyde when her cousin Mr Emerton claimed she had been married to him since her age of twelve! Dear Peregrine insisted on his marriage taking place! In this calamity I could not have supported myself without the help of my dear brother Charles. He managed the whole dreadful business and got her marriage to Mr Emerton dissolved, praise be to God!'

Her Ladyship ignored my words of comfort, and my enquiry as to the health of her brother's wife was met with a wave of the hand. 'Dear Mary! I see little of her, but Mrs Tryon! I hear she has been seen in the company of that rake, Lord Rivers! And poor Mr Tryon ill with the stone!'

At that his Lordship bade her be calm and I deemed it time to take my leave of them. I assured His Lordship that I was ever his humble servant, and should there be anything in my power to ease his unhappy situation,

---

The children of Judith Cullen (1626-1694) by her two husbands:

1. Mary Tryon (1650-c1679)
*   = 1) Sir Samuel Jones of Courteen Hall Northants*
*   = 2) The Honourable Charles Bertie*
2. Sarah Tryon (b.1651) = John Savile of Methley Hall co. York
3. James Tryon (1654-1685) = Margaret Stydolph.
*   (She married secondly Richard Savage, Earl Rivers)*
4. Samuel Tryon of Collyweston (1656-1712)
*   = 1) Elizabeth Hoste*
*   = 2) Christian Wenyeve*
5. Charles Cole (1664-1712) = Elizabeth Steane
6. Judith Cole (1666-1706) = Herbert Aubrey III of Clehonger

I would do it without hesitation. He smiled and I thought appeared rather reluctant to see me go. Even as I walked away from his quarters, I could still hear the sound of his wife's railing.

I reported the meeting to Thomas who promised to visit Lord Danby in my stead and to take him whatever necessities he lacked and the next day, I returned to Herefordshire.

***

As Deputy Lord Lieutenant of Hereford and Captain of Militia Horse I had the honour of accompanying His Grace the Duke of Beaufort, together with the Earl of Worcester, Sir John Talbot and several other Deputy Lieutenants of neighbouring counties to view the Militia Regiment of Monmouthshire. I directed my son and heir, as an ensign in our Militia Horse, to accompany me which he agreed to, with very bad grace – which reason I shall reveal in due course.

The sun shone on us as we made out way out of Hereford our horses caparisoned and pennants flying, along the old road south past Ross and into Monmouthshire. I privately considered that Earl's men made a rather motley group, straggling along rather than keeping pace with the leading drummers. Curious villagers on the way stared at the military procession and some waved their hats and shouted a 'hurrah' as we passed.

Soon we reached the old town, proud to be the birthplace of our glorious King Henry V. At the City Gate, the Mayor, resplendent in his robes and the rest of the Magistracy of Monmouth welcomed His Grace and bade the Company enter and we took our positions in front of the old castle.

The Earl of Worcester as Colonel of the Regiment and I as Captain stood in front of a stand of pikes and saluted His Grace and the Mayoral dignitaries. To my surprise, the troopers then demonstrated their discipline, marching and wheeling and counter-marching in good step to the drums and trumpets to such a variety of exercise that many of the common onlookers clapped their hands in admiration. The whole ended in a series of firings at which all the spectators cheered and hurrahed.

At that, the Mayor and the rest of the Magistracy of Monmouth formally invited His Grace to accept the Freedom of the place. The rest of us, attending His Grace were likewise made Freemen of that Corporation.

That done, His Grace and all who accompanied him, were invited to the Town Hall where a feast awaited us – chicken and rabbit, carp and pigeon pie, as I remember. The troopers were treated to as much cyder and Monmouth ale as they needed to slake their thirst, it being a warm day. Some were encouraged to let off several volleys at which the horses began rearing in fright, but all ended in good humour and we bade our hosts adieu and turned north for home.

My cheerful mood soon dissipated when my son and heir brought up the subject that had been consuming his waking thoughts for months now, Judith Cole. I told Herbert that I would never negotiate a marriage settlement with a man who had fought against the King – even although he was an intimate of one of the richest men in England.

In an unguarded moment, I brought up the possibility of the daughter of Sir Herbert Price, Master of the King's household and a distant cousin as a possible candidate for Herbert's hand, but this produced such a tirade that had he been younger and not so tall in stature, I would have taken the strap to him.

'Do you know what they call her?', he shouted, '"Fat Price"! Her father pays no debts! Why? Because she shares the Duke of York's bed! And as for the other candidate I heard you once mention to Mama, 'tis common knowledge in London that Sir Winston Churchill proffered his daughter to the Duke in return for a thousand pounds – of which he is now the richer!'

Hearing those dreadful words from the London gutter made me so angry that I refused to speak to my son for days, and would have cut him out of my will, had I been able. I cursed Fate, that had sent me such a scourge as a disobedient and ungrateful son and heir.

33. A New King

Hard on the heels of our return to Hereford came the news that our Gracious Monarch had died. King Charles and I were almost the same age and I remembered my father relating the story of his hiding in the oak tree at Boscobel and how I vowed that I would serve him all my life. The cushion with the silken oak leaves that my mother had so lovingly embroidered constantly reminded me of our family's dedication to the Royal cause. I felt the loss more than anyone and I refused to believe the story that he had converted to Catholicism on his deathbed.

Such rumours only served to foment strife in the land and to give encouragement to the followers of the King's bastard, the Duke of Monmouth who claimed his right to the throne. Our new King, James the Second, the late King's brother, believed as I did, that no unlawful title could ever be countenanced. His Majesty King James II sat on the throne by the Grace of God and Divine Law.

Everyone knew the Duke of Monmouth had always wanted to succeed his father and even being exiled to Holland had failed to discourage his ambition. With his uncle newly enthroned, and whispers of Exclusionists still being heard, he believed he had sufficient support in the country and made his play. He landed at Lyme Regis and issued a proclamation of his right to succeed his father. But neither that, nor his several thousand followers proved to be enough to win the day.

Royalist troops easily put down the uprising and he fled the battlefield. They dragged the Duke from his hiding place in a ditch in the New Forest to whence he had fled after the battle and took him to London. King James was deaf to his pleas for mercy and the would-be usurper was promptly executed. I was pleased to learn that Chief Justice Lord Jeffreys conducted the trials of the Duke's supporters with great severity. Some three hundred traitors met their death by hanging and quartering as a bloody lesson to others with similar intentions.

Soon after the coronation of his rightful Majesty King James II, my brother Godwin returned to these shores and married Jane Clark at Brampton Abbots, in the parish church so familiar to many of our Rudhall relations. She was a cheerful buxom wench who could neither read nor write but she would see to his every need. He promised her he would never go to sea again, but always longing to be near it and to hear its sound, he took up a position of Customs Officer at Rye in Sussex. His salary of £90 a year included a servant and a horse, a greater emolument than that enjoyed by many other younger sons.

It was hardly a quiet existence for him. The place was often overrun by smugglers and free traders who would take the law into their own hands and terrorise the town. Characteristically, Godwin seemed unconcerned at the hazardous nature of the position. When we were boys, he rarely showed fear. He would climb a tree higher then any other boy, daring us to follow him, and he could outrun any of us, young as he was.

His tales of his life at sea with Captain George Swanley, held my sons spellbound and I thanked God that none of them had any inclination to follow in his footsteps. I could only give the couple my blessing with a present of two brass candlesticks that had once graced Priors Court, my wife's early home.

At this time I had to find the money for a dower for my daughter Joyce, a quiet, serious young woman who had unaccountably insisted on marrying one Gilbert Hearne of Hereford, a scholar and a man of little account, although he held some manors and lands.

When the new King called Parliament, Mr Foley told me he had no desire to stand with me, but in so doing, he was not 'casting any aspersions on your undoubted abilities, Mr Aubrey', I remembered him saying. Other and more personal matters demanded his attention.

In fact I had no need of Mr Paul Foley's support as Mr Geers, a lawyer of my acquaintance had broached the same subject with me only a few days before. He did not evince the same firmness of opinion as I on the matter of Exclusion, nevertheless, we agreed to stand together as Representatives of the Freemen of Hereford.

So I made myself agreeable to as many Freemen of the City as I could, while having to spend as little money as possible in the process, for like Sir John Hoskyns and my old friend Sir John Morgan, the two Knights of the Shire, we all stood unopposed. Everyone knew my devotion to the rightful Monarch and our Established Church, and on the day the poll was declared, the voters confirmed my election once again to Westminster. Now I could more readily devote my energies to the new King, whom I vowed to serve to the utmost of my being.

We were bidden to attend His Majesty at Westminster on Tuesday the nineteenth of May at seven o'clock in the morning and I prepared for my journey to London in good time and with the greatest of pleasure.

Rather than stay in Thomas's uncomfortable lodgings, I accepted the invitation to stay with Mr Kingdon and his lady wife near Gray's Inn, a residence kindly provided by Sir Robert Holmes for Mrs Kingdon and her children to reside in when her husband was in Ireland. My wife viewed this act of kindness on the part of Mrs Kingdon with her customary suspicion and I had needs remind her that our families were bound, not only by blood, but now by money, my having been honoured by being included in Mr Kingdon's plan to lease out property at Ledbury.

I omitted to tell her that Thomas had given me some troublesome news. The disposal of the money from the farming of the Hearth Tax surplus arranged by Mr Kingdon's syndicate had come under scrutiny, resulting in Mr Kingdon and his partners being dismissed. They were ordered to refund the several thousand pounds of which people claimed they had cheated the Crown.

His creditors were hounding him yet according to Thomas, Mrs Kingdon was still spending lavishly on clothes and jewels. I knew that tales often got distorted in the telling and re-telling and that Thomas was only reporting gossip. Nevertheless, I vowed to determine the truth or otherwise myself at the earliest opportunity.

My acquaintance with Mrs Kingdon had been limited to the infrequent visits she had made to Herefordshire to visit members of my wife's family. She was a well-built wench, now still only about twenty-four years old and with a brood of children, four daughters and a son and heir called Edward. She had a very ready smile, and behind her bright eyes I detected a hint of mockery, which sometimes discomforted me.

Nevertheless, sitting in her parlour, *en famille*, the first day after my arrival in London, her solicitations as to my comfort and her total agreement with my every utterance caused me to adjust my assessment of her character.

When I commented to Mr Kingdon, that first evening, that the generosity of the wealthy Governor of the Isle of Wight knew no bounds, he responded with what I could only describe as a 'smirk', and looked quickly at Mrs Kingdon, His wife in turn looked down with great intensity at the embroidery in her hands and I thought I detected a blush cross her ample bosom.

Mr Kingdon seemed happy to regale me with stories of Sir Robert's bravery at sea, how attached he was to the Duke of York as he was then and how he had often entertained His Majesty in his large mansion in Yarmouth, to which they had both been honoured guests.

He spoke at length of his frequent visits to Ireland and he how enjoyed the friendship – nay, close friendship - of Lord Ranalagh and Lord Arran whose father the Duke of Ormonde, was Lord Lieutenant of the Kingdom and a dignified old Royalist to his fingertips. Gossip incurred by the behaviour of my wife's niece or not, her husband's friendship with such honourable Royalists impressed me immeasurably.

I tentatively raised the subject of the theatre, and remarked how his late Majesty had so enjoyed its pleasures. It was now Mr Kingdon's turn to appear discomforted, in fact his expression quite darkened. Believing myself to be a good judge of character, I deduced that things theatrical had been the subject of some marital discord. 'We are both devotees of the theatre,' responded Mrs Kingdon, 'are we not, my love?'

She smiled brightly and then as if struck by a sudden thought said, 'My husband has been honoured with a gift of a copy of Mrs Behn's latest poems, signed by the playwright herself. It contains three State poems she has composed, one on the death of our dear departed Late Sovereign, one to the Queen Dowager, and a Pindaric Poem on the Happy Coronation. Pray read them, I am sure they will please you.'

She handed me the book of verse and I promised her I would give them my most earnest attention, especially those devoted to our late Monarch and the present King.

Talk then moved to the imminent meeting of the Commons, for in that first Parliament of King James II, Mr Kingdon had been returned as a Member for Bedwyn thanks to the influence of Lord Bruce. It was thus convenient for us to go together to Westminster, when required.

Each day we took a hackney coach there, Mr Kingdon confessing that ill-health prevented him from walking he was wont to do. He allowed me to pay the twelve pence that each journey cost.

One of the first persons I sought out on the first day of our assemblage, was Lord Danby, for he had been released from the Tower after five unhappy years' incarceration and had been bidden to take his seat in the House of Lords. When we came face to face at last, his appearance gave me concern, for his stature was even leaner and his face considerably paler. He favoured me with a wan smile and enquired after my family in the kindest of manner but I could sense that his mind was on other and more urgent matters.

Sir Robert Holmes had been returned as a Member for Winchester and Mr Kingdon did me the honour of introducing me to his kind friend. I was privileged to meet a fellow Royalist and one who had served so bravely in His Majesty's Army during the Troubles.

I found Sir Robert to be a large man, dressed in a richly embroidered silk jacket in the latest style, with a beard speckled with grey and a rugged, weather-beaten face, doubtless the result of his many years at sea in the service of the Crown. He took little interest in my protestations of admiration of his many heroic exploits but rather seemed more interested in the health and welfare of 'Our Dear Theodosia', as he called Mrs Kingdon.

There was little other chance of my talking to the man who had entertained His Majesty often at his great mansion at Yarmouth, because soon affairs in the House commanded our attention.

One day as we sat in Mr Kingdon's dining room I could not help but notice my host's pallid face had taken on more colour and he demanded another bottle of wine be placed on the table. 'I drink to my Lord Ranelagh! And the Devil take Sir Stephen Fox!'[1]. At that, Mrs Kingdon caught my eye and smiled broadly but my host bade me hold my questions, for on the morrow my curiosity would be satisfied and all would be revealed.

He then pleaded tiredness and retired, leaving Mrs Kingdon and me together, alone. She seized the opportunity of begging me to give her the latest intelligence of her dear kinsmen in Herefordshire. I confess that enjoying Mr Kingdon's excellent wine while expounding on such as I knew of the Brydges family, and then enlightening her on more important matters such as my belief in Kingship, gave me the greatest of pleasures – particularly having such a young and attentive listener as Mrs Kingdon.

The following day sure enough, to the amazement of several Members, Mr Kingdon was elected to the Committee to inspect the disbandment accounts, which confusion dated back to the earlier Parliaments. Furthermore, his syndicate to farm the Hearth Tax surplus was reinstated and extended for five years on the payment of £30,000.

Gasps and raised voices greeted this announcement.

In private, Mr Kingdon refused to enlighten me as to the details of this arrangement – they were confidential, he claimed - and the next day, as he had hinted, Sir Stephen Fox was dismissed and Lord Ranelagh took his place as Paymaster. Tongues inevitably wagged at this turn of events and I heard that Mr Kingdon might be appointed His Lordship's Deputy.

Mr Kingdon still refused to discuss this change of his fortune with me, always pleading tiredness and I confess, the grey pallor had returned to his visage and Mrs Kingdon was even more solicitous of his immediate comfort. I considered him fortunate to have such a young and comely helpmeet.

During the days the House sat, I busied myself on numerous Committees. One of the first was to consider an imposition be laid on wines and vinegar towards the supply for the repairs of the Navy and Ordnance. When it was passed into law, it brought a smile to the face of Mr Pepys[2] of the Navy Office and Member for Harwich with whom I had become acquainted.

He and I both sat on the Committee ordered to inspect the Journals of the House and report what we thought to be expunged or revived. Another called us to consider the Bill for erecting a new Parish, to be called the Parish of St James within the liberty of Westminster. Included in the latter Committee was Sir Christopher Wren[3] still greatly concerned with aspects of re-structuring London after the Great Fire. Both Bills passed into law after being carried up to the Lords for their Concurrence.

I am proud to say that I soon gained a reputation of always speaking honestly and remained, as people came to describe me, a 'passionate Welshman' with a Celtic taste for emotional rhetoric. I was honoured to read the Report from the Committee on the Bill on the Improvement of Tillage. Thus many concerns of national importance exercised my mind during those months of May and June.

Two faces I was particularly pleased to see were my old friend and Fellow Archer, Sir Joseph Williamson now the Member for Thetford, looking older and more drawn, and the Honourable Mr Charles Bertie, Lord Danby's brother-in-law whose acquaintance I had first made years before and in happier times.

To my surprise, the latter sought me out one day, and before I could enquire after the health of his sister Lady Danby, he bade me give him news of my son and heir. I told Mr Bertie it did us great honour for young Herbert to be the subject of such a kind enquiry and that thanks be to God, he was thriving and that he continued to regale us with accounts of his visits to Sir Robert Clayton's impressive seat, Marden Park. At that, Mr Bertie smiled slyly, 'And has he given you full details of the young woman who caught his fancy while on one of his visits there? Mistress Cole, I believe is her name?'

His question troubled me more than I care to admit but I believe I dignified it with a simple and short, 'Yes, Mr Bertie, he has.' To my great relief, Sir Joseph caught my eye and the moment moved on, easily allowing the unpleasant subject to be changed. I vowed to have words with young Herbert as soon as possible.

I was pleased to see the last of London, but not of Mrs Kingdon who begged me to carry many messages from her to her dear kith and kin in the county.

Unfortunately, the onerous journey home and my wife's incessant questions concerning her niece soon brought on a throbbing in my head which necessitated immediate physic and several days in the dark silence of my chamber before the balance of my humours was restored.

---

1. Sir Stephen Fox (1627-1716), financier and government official. As Paymaster, he accumulated considerable wealth.

2. Samuel Pepys, (1633-1703), M.P., diarist and naval administrator. He served as Secretary to the Admiralty and was for a term, President of the Royal Society.

3. Sir Christopher Wren (1632-1723), M.P. and architect. He was Professor of Astronomy at Oxford and had a wide range of interests including mathematics, optics, anatomy and medicine. He played an important part in the foundation of the Royal Society and became its President in 1680. Charles II appointed him Surveyor-General and he was the principal architect for the rebuilding of London after the Great Fire.

34. Ireland

At the Assizes, which duty forced me to attend, the Foreman of the Grand Jury, a Papist, if ever there was one, tendered an address. In it, he thanked the King for his Declaration of Indulgence, but had the temerity to omit entirely, His Majesty's favour to the Church of England and the gracious promises he has made to support it. For that reason, I had no hesitation in having it rejected. On these Royal assurances and promises of favouring our Church, those of our persuasion pinned our fervent hopes.

Then, the worst fears of those of us who dreaded Catholicism but who considered ourselves loyal subjects and devout Anglicans, seemed about to be realised. His Majesty promoted Catholics to governmental and military posts and obliged the universities to admit them.

Such decisions contravened the Test Act which required all civil and military office holders to take the Oaths of Allegiance and Supremacy, and receive the Sacrament after the forms of the Church of England. Because of his Catholicism, His Majesty himself, when Duke of York had been obliged to resign as Lord High Admiral even after his success in the Dutch wars. Now he used his Royal prerogative to nullify the Test Act. We watched with increasing concern His Majesty's Catholic sympathies and his antagonism towards our Church. Unrest and seditious whisperings gathered momentum.

As a Member of Parliament, I would soon have to pass the fire ordeal, and be tested with the burning torch – to choose - my King or my Church? The dilemma in which I found myself gave me constant sleepless nights.

In the midst of all this, I was destined to be deceived yet again, I believe that men who are themselves utterly trustworthy, and I name myself among such, often fail to detect untrustworthiness in others. The rents from Ledbury failed to meet the total amount that Mr Kingdon had assured me would soon be mine to enjoy. My letters to him demanding an explanation remained unanswered, while, according to Thomas and other talk now circulating in Hereford, Mrs Kingdon continued to luxuriate in her companionship with Sir Robert Holmes.

By now Joyce was compelled to concede that Mrs Kingdon's

upbringing and character had contributed much to the unsavoury nature of her husband's reputation and for once I was reluctantly forced to agree with her.

None of this was any consolation, for with all my other financial ventures, for some unaccountable reason, insufficient money was never forthcoming and the burden of debt still hung heavy on me. It irked me more than somewhat to remember that Mr Kingdon was still enjoying his £1,000 per annum as Commissioner for Revenue in Ireland, but if rumours as to his failing health were true, then it would not be for long.

At this point, fortune appeared to shine on me, ironically through the demise of Lemuel Kingdon and mercifully through the kindness of my Lord Rochester.

In the last few years of his appointment to the Irish Revenue Commission, Mr Kingdon had taken over with him two of his friends to that Kingdom, Mr Genew and Joyce's cousin Mr Brydges. Whispers soon began circulating that Mr Genew had been siphoning off £2,000 a quarter of the King's money and although the Commissioners suspected him, they could prove nothing.

Mr Genew fell suddenly ill and died and soon afterwards, and not long after my stay with them in London, Mr Kingdon's health fell into a decline. As soon as I heard word of his imminent demise, I considered it expedient to travel all the way back to London, onerous as it was for me at that time of year, firstly to attend his funeral and pay my last respects, and secondly to call on Lord Rochester.

I had written to His Lordship immediately on hearing the news of Mr Kingdon's death, offering myself for the position in my kinsman's stead. I knew that loyalty and trustworthiness were the strongest points in my character, in contrast to that of the late lamented Commissioner.

Mr Kingdon was buried at St Giles in the Fields on a freezing February day and many were the thoughts I had during the service of wishing to be back at my hearth and home at Clehonger, seated in front of a warm fire.

The grieving Mrs Kingdon, adorned in black, was supported on one side by her son Edward and on the other, Sir Robert Holmes, limping awkwardly. Behind trailed the four orphan daughters and the deceased's mother, Mrs Jane Kingdon, weeping copiously and blaming the Irish for taking her son from this world.

Salt & Silk

Much was to be learnt by my attending the funeral. Mr Kingdon had made Sir Edward Seymour an executor of his will, which made me more sanguine about the future of my holding at Ledbury in which syndicate Mr Kingdon was also still heavily involved.

Sir Edward was a known Exclusionist and it always gave me great pleasure to remember the episode when as Speaker of the Commons, he turned to that immoral man Colonel Birch and said, 'Sir, think you not that it is indecent to brush your beard without the use of a looking glass?' Members laughed and Colonel Birch, vanity being one of his many faults, reddened with anger at being the butt of such a jibe.

As for Sir Robert Holmes, he had just been given a Commission to command a squadron to go to the West Indies for the suppression of pirates, but observing his painful gait I wondered how he could ever survive another sea voyage, and part from the young Widow Kingdon at this unhappy time.

Within a week after my return home, I was advised that the position on the Irish Revenue Commission, left vacant by the death of Mr Lemuel Kingdon was to be filled by Mr Herbert Aubrey, Esq. of Clehonger. Even my dear wife wept with joy at the prospect of my receiving £1,000 per annum, payable quarterly. I felt that I had come to a turning point in my life and that last I would be adequately compensated for my devotion to His Majesty.

My son and heir had removed himself from my orbit and was a frequent guest of Sir Robert Clayton at his seat of Marden Park, when he was not attending his new-found friends in Northamptonshire – and Mr Charles Cole in Hampshire, the brother of the orphaned Miss Cole of whom he was still enamoured. Mr Cole had in fact written to me, in somewhat stilted terms, extending an invitation to visit his estate at Lyss in Hampshire, but I replied that I was unable to avail myself of the pleasure of accepting his hospitality because the heavy duties associated with my appointment to the Irish Revenue Commission.

Strangely enough others, particularly Lord Danby's brother-in-law Mr Bertie, found young Herbert to be a most amenable young man, so he reported to me on the few occasions we chanced to meet. Nevertheless, I refused to be drawn on the subject of my son and heir, especially with a man so blind to young Herbert's many failings. As for Lord Danby himself, he had recovered from his years in the Tower and had returned to his own hearth and home at Wallingford House.

Young Brydges, who would do anything for his older brother, now took on much of Herbert's responsibilities of running the estates while Reginald was attending Balliol College. I had made this possible with great difficulty, for to have a son enter the Church of England meant a great deal to me, especially as His Majesty's sympathy and leaning towards those of the Roman faith was becoming more and more evident.

With trunks packed and preparations complete, I bade a fond farewell to my family and set off across the sea to Ireland, unfortunately before the winter winds had abated.

After a rough crossing, which sorely affected my stomach, I took comfort from the warmth with which my fellow Commissioners greeted me once I arrived in Dublin. One of them, Lord Longford confessed to me in confidence that he was relieved to have an honest man in their midst. Such trust in my character, lifted my spirits and I thanked God that my worth was to be recognised at last.

One of my first duties was to pay my respects to the Earl of Clarendon, Lord Lieutenant of Ireland whose brother, Lord Rochester had so kindly taken my application to His Majesty and recommended me for the position. During the course of conversation, I raised the subject of Mr Kingdon, at which name His Lordship frowned.

'I hesitate to speak ill of the dead, Mr Aubrey, I am not surprised at any ill thing which is discovered of Mr Kingdon, because I never had a good opinion of the man. Mr Kingdon was corrupt and rapacious and there was no living with him without submitting to him.' I admitted to His Lordship, that thanks to an unhappy set of circumstances, and trusting him as I did as a kinsman, I stood to lose a considerable sum of money on a scheme which he assured me would bring in a good return.

After politely commiserating, he concluded, 'Well, I am glad to see you among us, Mr Aubrey.' And with that, His Lordship changed the subject to more immediate matters and soon bade me goodbye.

I knew he had more weighty things on his mind, not the least being the Earl of Tyrconnel, a rigid Catholic and Commander of the Military Forces in Ireland - and a long-time friend and confidente of His Majesty. The Earl was hell bent on promoting Catholics to important positions in Ireland, and in the process, arrogantly overriding the wishes of the Lord Lieutenant.

Thus I became one of the Commissioners of the King's revenues in Ireland, joining my fellow Commissioners in managing and collecting all the monies payable to the King from his many properties in that Kingdom. I soon settled in and found my fellow Commissioners to be helpful and courteous, especially Lord Longford and the Secretary to the Commissioners Mr Ellis, a tall, earnest young man who greeted me kindly, and I almost venture to add, with relief.

But two matters turned my attention from these most immediate concerns. The first was a tiredness that seemed to overwhelm me after the slightest of exertions and I came to dread travelling more than a few miles from the lodgings I had taken in Dublin. The second related to the final settlement of the Hearth Tax money which amount had not been finalised before my departure for Ireland. On the strength of the latter, I requested leave which I was given permission to take in April 1686.

Unhappily, the Hearth Money accounts were in such a confusion, that I was unable to resolve the final amount to my satisfaction in the two weeks allowed me. To ease my comfort, I resolved to bring my wife Joyce and my younger daughter little Betty back with me to Dublin. Little Betty danced with joy at the prospect, but my wife found numerous reasons why they should remain at home, but I refused to be dissuaded from my decision.

Once back in Dublin after a fortunately less onerous journey than Joyce had anticipated, Mr Ellis who had worked under my fellow Archer Sir Joseph Williamson many years before, made it his business to see to the ease and welfare of my wife and daughter for which I could only thank and bless him.

35. Jacobite Suspect

In the meantime, it had became apparent that tension was mounting sharply between the Irish Catholics and the Irish Protestants. The Earl of Tyrconnel was working to put control of all Irish affairs, even the army, into the hands of Roman Catholics. In so doing, he was busy undermining the efforts of the Earl of Clarendon, who was endeavouring to ally the fears of the Protestants and keep the status quo.

It was comforting to know that the Earl of Clarendon's brother, Lord Rochester was in London and at least still had the ear of His Majesty. I believed that the King still grieved over the death of his first wife Anne, their sister, notwithstanding the influence his second wife, Mary of Modena was having over him, persuading him to promote Catholic interests in all quarters.

I had been only a few months in Ireland when I developed a wen, a sebaceous cyst on my scalp. Such an affliction caused me great discomfort under my wig and it was recommended that I obtain a plaster from Paris called *Emplastrum Mirabile*, which one particular apothecary sold there. Being sympathetic of my plight, my colleague George Trumbull agreed to beg a favour of his brother Sir William, who had recently been sent to France as Envoy Extraordinary, and entreated him to obtain the medication for me.

The plaster took months to reach me in Dublin, and when it did, I seemed hardly to help my affliction. In fact, I became more and more lethargic and found it increasingly difficult to collect my thoughts on a subject.

Even in Ireland, my enemies continued to spread rumour and innuendo about me and a few of my fellow Commissioners began to find fault with my efforts. But such matters paled into insignificance when compared to the growing rivalry between the Earl of Tyrconnel and the Earl of Clarendon.

Worse, we heard that Lord Rochester had fallen out of favour with His Majesty and had been dismissed. It took only three weeks after that for the Earl of Clarendon to learn that he had been recalled to London and that the Earl of Tyrconnel had been appointed Lord Lieutenant of Ireland in his place.

Salt & Silk

Such ignominy! I grieved for both brothers, upright men who had served His Majesty with such devotion, as indeed had I.

I too, was obliged to return to England to clear my final account of the Hearth Money which was still outstanding. Joyce begged to return with me, but I bade her stay and asked my good friend Mr Ellis to see to her comfort and well-being. He vowed it would give him great pleasure and immediately called on my wife to assuage her concerns.

Back in Hereford, the topics on everyone's lips were the Test and Penal Laws that His Majesty seemed determined to repeal. The King wanted Catholics in all positions of influence, even in the Universities.

The Foreman of the Grand Jury, a new convert, had drawn up an Address supporting the Repeal. He wanted my consent to it, but to his ire, I naturally refused put my signature. It made no mention of His Majesty's favour to the Church of England and his gracious promises to support it. I knew there would be consequences as a result of this, but many of many friends agreed with me.

Several of my acquaintance had laid down their commissions, my old friend Sir John Morgan being one of them. It was ever my opinion that an ill man can never make a good subject or a good friend and I would not be thought false to such eminent interests.

Then to my despair, we heard that the Queen was with child again. Even although she had brought forth a number of dead babies, a lusty son meant the existence of a future sovereign raised in the Catholic faith. By now, many people believed that the King's daughter Mary, heiress presumptive to the throne and her Protestant husband William of Orange would one day became Queen and King of England.

But in the event of the present Queen bearing a son, God's will lay in the lawful male heir of our anointed Sovereign. Besides, Mary was a woman, and what kind of a man was her husband William? He was not an Englishmen, in spite of the validity of his faith. Everywhere I searched, I saw a dark, bleak hole. I had been saved from 'the ordeal of fire' by moving to Dublin, but I could not escape the turmoil these future possibilities produced in my mind.

Once back in Ireland after another difficult crossing, my family greeted me with tears of joy, but all was not well in that Kingdom and I knew it was only a matter of time before matters came to a head. Then, on the tenth day of June in 1688, they did; Queen Mary gave His Majesty a son and heir to the English throne and named him James Francis Edward Stuart.

There were cheers from many in Dublin, but almost at once, an ominous rumour circulated in London and we soon heard it whispered in Ireland. The Queen had given birth to another still-born and in desperation, a substitute baby boy had been smuggled into her lying-in chamber in a warming pan.

I resisted the temptation to believe such nonsense. All those in official attendance at the lying-in would soon disprove it and His Majesty would never be a party to such a ruse. It mattered only that now, Mary and her husband Prince William could no longer be heirs presumptive to the throne. They had been superseded by the King's son, the rightful heir to the throne of England who was now the future James the Third.

Tension mounted everywhere, particularly in London, where we heard that suspicion and antagonism towards our Sovereign was the greatest. Matters were not much better in Ireland. Whole battalions of Protestant soldiers were discharged, leaving many civilians to the mercy of marauders. The country was fast sinking into ruin and despair. Rumour had it that the Earl of Tyrconnel had arranged for Ireland to be made a French protectorate, but I could never believe that His Majesty would countenance such a plan.

Daily we waited for news from London, uncertain which stories to believe and which were merely malicious gossip. Had Prince William of Orange in fact been secretly invited to England? Names of the Earl of Shrewsbury and my old friend Lord Danby were linked with this rumour. Had the Prince landed with a military force? Had he been warmly welcomed in London? Was it a fact that our anointed King had been arrested and held in the course of trying to escape? Were the Royal family now safely in Paris? Had His Sovereign Majesty thrown the Great Seal, his symbol of authority into the River Thames?

To my dismay, some of the wildest stories were later confirmed as fact. Such events were beyond comprehension and I feared a bloody outcome, remembering the civil strife of my youth. I prayed for the safety of our Royal family, and tried to untangle the turmoil of my thoughts to my dear wife, often well into the early hours.

She bore my ordeal with great fortitude. Eventually, she persuaded me that I should beg leave and that we should return to Clehonger, at least for a little while, 'until your health improves' she said. We both knew we would never set foot in Ireland again, nor did we want to. Social order had deteriorated into chaos under the Earl of Tyrconnel's erratic rule and even Trinity College had been invaded and all the horses and arms removed.

A few days before we were to board the boat that was to take us to Chester, we heard that our true Monarch, James II, was to arrive in Dublin. My daughter Betty begged me to come with her in our carriage to try to catch a glimpse of him, and reluctantly I agreed. We gathered in few of our loyal servants for protection and set out towards the castle.

His Majesty was carrying the Sword of State before him as he entered its precincts. High over the castle fluttered a flag, pronouncing, 'Nor or never, now and for ever'. Some of the waiting populace cheered and hurrahed their hats to his Majesty. Many stood glumly silent. Betty cheered and waved from the carriage window, but it saddened me to look at yet another doomed Monarch. My thoughts raced back to the time when his father, King Charles, had ridden into Hereford in triumph and waved his hat and smiled at me.

The King and his forces soon left Dublin and headed north for the Boyne. We were now at war with France. It boded ill for us all. Seven Peers of the Realm, Lord Danby among them, had indeed invited Prince William of Orange to England, and before we could prepare for our departure, it was forced upon us; I had been relieved of my position as a Commissioner of the Revenue. It only remained now for the three of us to face the worsening weather and return to England without delay, and in safety.

Even in my illness, my enemies aimed their darts, for as Betty had overheard, directions had been given to our landlord at Chester that I should be arrested. There was no escape, for Betty had no sooner repeated the words, than there came a loud bang at our door. Joyce wailed in fear and there was nothing to be done, but open it and face the consequences.

The Landlord, with two men at arms bade us come at once to the Mayor's house, where we were to be detained until further orders. It took us some time to leave the inn, Joyce having swooned, but soon revived after an application of smelling salts. At last we were taken by coach – but accompanied by the armed men - to the Mayor's house. He greeted us civilly enough, although I detected a degree of uncertainty, especially when I demanded of him paper, pen and ink.

I despatched a short note to my Lord Danby, telling him of our predicament, advising him of my ill-health and begging him to use his influence to free us. In less than a week, thanks to my Lord Danby, instructions for our release were issued, and the Mayor advised us that we were free to leave.

On our arrival at back Clehonger, weary and relieved, my son Herbert greeted us amicably. My wife of course was overjoyed to be home and to see him again. I was agreeably surprised to learn that all the tenants had paid their dues and that the estates were in reasonable order, mostly I later learned, with the help of my youngest son Brydges, now a strapping seventeen-year-old, grown taller and stronger in our absence. With a great deal of effort on my part, I resumed my duties as one of the Deputy Lieutenants of the County.

One day, I again broached the subject of a wife for Herbert, but he immediately reverted to his old arrogant expression and disrespectful air.

'Do not trouble yourself Sir, as you well know I have already found one – it is Miss Cole, whose late father I believe you met – and spurned the overtures of her brother to discuss a marriage settlement!' He turned on his heel and stormed out of the room. My fury at his impertinence knew no bounds. My wife burst into tears when she heard this intelligence and I was obliged to take to my bed until my apoplexy had subsided. My humours were again in discord.

Herbert would contribute nothing more to this subject, only repeating his new found admiration for King William, which I knew he did just to vex me. Many of my friends and kin, and others throughout the country, thought as I. In my heart, I thanked God that I was not a clergyman, having to break my oath of allegiance to King James II and formally, and in the sight of God, take an oath to King William III.

Reginald was still at Oxford, and Brydges swore he knew nothing about Herbert's woman, only that Herbert had often been away visiting friends in London and then latterly in Edmonton. My daughter Joyce, now Mrs Hearne and the mother of a young son, had no inkling as to her character and demeanour.

One day, I commanded my son and heir to attend me in my study. Nothing much in it had changed since my own father had summoned me

Salt & Silk

thence to give me the news of his being fined for Delinquency. As I sat behind the old desk, waiting for the knock, I remembered my sister Anne and I discovering the 'priest's hole' hidden in the wall above the chest of drawers and our hiding there during the Troubles, all those years ago.

I was brought sharply to the present by my son knocking and opening the door even before I had time to utter the words, 'Enter!'. Nevertheless, I deemed it wise to ignore his pre-emptory behaviour and bade him be seated.

The look on his face spoke volumes and uppermost I saw antagonism.

'I know you have bidden me here to speak of Judith Cole, whom I intend to marry, and I wish to say this: the honourable Charles Bertie, whose acquaintance you have made, and who knows the financial position in which you find yourself, is much in favour of the match.' I could say nothing to this, so held my tongue.

'Her mother's brother was the late Sir Abraham Cullen, a Member of Parliament, and her uncle by marriage, Sir James Rushout, a fellow Member of Parliament whom you may remember in the Oxford Parliament, has seen no objection to the match, in spite of the unfortunate reputation of some of our kinsmen such as Mr Kingdon – sir.' I said nothing to this comment.

'Mrs Cole has no objection to the match, and as Mr Cole has departed this world, it will now be necessary for you to consider the marriage settlement with her brother Mr Charles Cole.' His arrogant tone, emblazened me into fury.

'I have no wish to meet Mr Cole or his sister!' However, he paled in his discomfort when I raised the matter of the girl's dowry. 'There is very little to discuss on that head, Sir,' he said.

Under such circumstances, I told him I refused absolutely to give my consent to the union. For days after that encounter, Herbert would speak only when directly spoken to, and then only in surly monosyllables. My wife spent much of her time in tears and even Betty seemed not to be her usual cheerful self in my company.

A gloom settled over the whole house and when we heard the news from Ireland that King William had defeated his father-in-law King James at the Boyne, I could only walk the well-trodden path to our parish church and pray for us all.

Woes come not in single file. If I had ever forgotten the unfortunate business with Roger Vaughan, another related matter came to a head at this time to remind me and to follow me to the grave and beyond. Roger's half-sister Mary Cornewall had married Gilbert Nicholetts junior. Not only was the marriage a disaster, but the acrimony simmering between Gilbert and his father, Gilbert Nicholetts senior, resulted in a series of legal cases. Six months before he died, Gilbert junior made provision for his wife, their only son, also named Gilbert, and five daughters. He bequeathed his estate valued at £500 - £600 plus his personal estate to me and Robert Price and our heirs, on the understanding that as trustees, we would pay the several debts, legacies, portions and annuities.

Such a great responsibility only added to my depression and unhappiness, and I could only hand over the burden to my son and heir and pray to God that he would find the means to do justice to the trust that had been put in me.

Knowing that I would soon be meeting my Maker and confessing my manifold sins, I first needed to put my own affairs in order and to write my will.

I had much to occupy my mind, not least the future of the Royal

---

Sir Walter Pye = Joane Rudhall
(1571-1635) | (c1584-1625)
Frances Pye = (1635) 1) Henry Vaughan of Bredwardine and Moccas
                                                 |
Roger Vaughan (1641-1672)

= (1650) 2) Edward Cornewall of Berrington (1613-1709)
                                 |
Henry Cornewall M.P. (c1655-1716)

= 1) Margarita Huyssen (c1659-1692)
= 2) Susanna Williams (b.c1670)

Frances Cornewall (b.c1659)
= William Lingen (b.c1657)

Mary Cornewall (c1668-1702)
= Gilbert Nicholetts (c1666-1691)

Salt & Silk

House of Stuart. All my life I have remained faithful to the Church of England as it is by law established; I have never been tempted to succumb to Roman Catholicism. I penned the words that encapsulated my deepest belief, declaring in my testament that,

> *'it admits not rebellion against a lawful sovereign, upon the most sanctified pretence or temptation whatever'.*

In spite of many temptations and a host of difficulties, I have tried to follow this precept and live my life decently and honourably. I have but one regret, that of leaving my poor wife burdened with the debts that I have incurred. Thoughts of my son and heir always cast a pall over my mood as the days drew in and winter approached. Soon a constant tiredness enveloped me as I lost count of the hours, at times hardly being able to rise from my bed.

At the end, Joyce was there, as always, holding my hand. Flanked on either side of her were my daughters Betty and Joyce and a man I took to be Joyce's husband Gilbert Hearne. Opposite stood my sons Brydges and Reginald, now grown so much taller. Thinking that I had failed to understand his words, Reginald, with Prayer Book in hand, reiterated several times that he had successfully matriculated from Balliol College. I could only nod my approval, thanking God in my thoughts.

When I looked around the room for my son and heir, my wife appeared uneasy. 'Herbert's left Clehonger, he's gone north to Northamptonshire - a'courting Mistress Cole,' she admitted at last.

At that, I could only close my eyes and sigh my last breath of this life.

APPENDIX A

Events in Morgan Aubrey's Lifetime

1527

Morgan Aubrey born Llanfrynach. Henry VIII has been on the throne for 18 years.

1528

Morgan's cousin William Aubrey born Cantref.

1531

Henry VII recognised as Supreme Head of the Church in England. 'Halley's Comet seen.

1532

Anne Boleyn crowned Queen, Pope ex-communicates Henry VIII.

1536

Queen Anne Boleyn executed, Henry VIII marries Jane Seymour.

1537

Queen Jane Seymour dies after birth of Prince Edward (later Edward VI).

1540

Henry VIII marries Anne of Cleves. Marriage annulled. King Henry marries Catherine Howard.

1545

Morgan goes to London about now. Works for his uncle John Aubrey, a clothworker.

1546

Henry VIII dies, is succeeded by his son by Jane Seymour, Edward VI.

1553

Lady Jane Grey Queen proclaimed queen; deposed nine days later. Mary becomes Queen of England.

1554

Morgan begins his apprenticeship as a Salter with James Peel.

1556

Morgan's uncle John Aubrey takes out case against Thomas Morgan Aubrey.

1557

Queen Mary dies, Queen Elizabeth succeeds her.

1560

19 December 1560 Morgan received into the Company of Salters and marries widow Joan Holman née Vaux about now.

1561

Morgan moves into Candlewick Street and begins trading in cloth.

1562

Queen Elizabeth nearly dies of smallpox.

1563

Plague hits London 20,000 people die. 25 May 1563 Margery Aubrey baptised at St Mary Abchurch.

1565

21 May 1565 Morgan's servant Joan Sheffell buried; 15 Jun 1565 Margery buried at St Mary Abchurch; Morgan stands Suretor in Court of Orphans.

1568

Morgan in London subsidy rolls assessed at £60.

1569

9 Nov 1569 Morgan's son William baptised.

1571

5 Feb 1571/2 Morgan's daughter Katherine baptised.

1572

Morgan recorded as 'Salter alias Citizen & Woolen Draper' of London; 20 Aug 1572 another William baptised.

1578

Hopkin Aubrey, Morgan's brother makes his will.

1579

26 February 1579/80 Morgan's son Samuel Aubrey baptised.

1580

Administration of will of Morgan's brother Hopkin to his sister Joan & husband William Taylor.

1582

Morgan in Subsidy Rolls as wealthiest in the Parish: worth £50 in goods, £10 p.a. in land & with property valued at £60. Taxed at 50 shillings.

1584

Morgan signs as a Suretor in the Court of Orphans.

1586

Mary Queen of Scots executed at Fotheringay

1587

Morgan negotiates marriage of daughter Katherine to Francis Bevans.

1588

Katherine aged 16 marries Francis Bevans at St Mary Abchurch. The 'invincible' Spanish Armada defeated.

1589

Morgan stands Suretor in Court of Orphans. Morgan richer, taxed at 60 shillings.

1590

Francis Bevans an Advocate. Bad harvests throughout the 1590s.

1592

Sir John Perrott dies in the Tower; Katherine's son Aubrey Bevans born; Plague kills 15,000 people in London.

1593

John Penry executed 1593; Francis Bevans represents Bishop's Castle in Herefordshire, 6 Jul 1593; Samuel enters St John's college Oxford aged 14.

1594

Morgan plaintif & Citizen of London & Salter; Morgan buys Dorstone & Clehonger; William Aubrey buys Stretford & Burleton; Thomas Knyvet conveys lease of Osterlow to Morgan.

1595

Dr William Aubrey dies; Sir Walter Raleigh sails to Guyana to seek 'El Dorado'.

1596

The Earl of Essex's successful expedition to Cadiz.

1599

Samuel admitted to Middle Temple aged c20 as son & heir of Morgan Aubrey of London, esq 1 Jan 1698/9; Morgan buys Bridgecourt Farm from Francis Bevans.

1600

Morgan and Samuel in court over Bridgecourt lease; Sir Gelly Merrick hanged at Tyburn.

1602

Francis Bevans dies and Katherine, now c31, marries Sir William Herbert, aged c63, 6 July 1602; Samuel marries Joyce Rudhall at Brampton Abbotts 13 Sep 1602.

1603

Death of Elizabeth I, succeeded by James VI of Scotland; heavy outbreak of plague; Morgan's grandson Herbert Aubrey born.

1605

Gunpowder plot; Katherine Aubrey baptised at St Mary Abchurch; Samuel's daughter Joane born.

1607

James I gives new charter to Salters; 2 Jun 1607 Morgan sworn in as Alderman; Samuel's son Morgan born.

1608

Morgan Aubrey dies, buried at St Mary Abchurch 10 January; his son Samuel Aubrey is now head of the family He is c29.

Events in Herbert Aubrey II's Lifetime

1630
Herbert Aubrey II baptised 27 Feb 1630/1

1631
His sister Mary baptised 15 Feb 1631/2

1632
His sister Elizabeth baptised 26 Jan 1632/3

1634
His brother Mathew baptised 9 Nov 1634

1635
His sister Judith born.

1636
His brother Godwin baptised 9 Jun 1636; his grandfather Mathew Bedell makes his will.

1637
His brother Thomas baptised 26 Oct 1637.

1638
His grandmother Lady Aubrey dies.

1639
Bad harvests throughout the 1630s.

1641
Catholic rebellion in Ireland. Herbert's uncle Morgan killed on the bridge at Portadown; anti-Catholic hysteria sweeps England.

1642
Charles I raises his standard at Nottingham castle; civil wars begin; Sir Samuel borrows £30 from Peter Wyatt.

1643
Sir William Waller takes Hereford; Herbert's grandfather taken prisoner.

1644
Sir Henry Lingen in command of the siege of Brampton Bryan Castle.

1645

Sir Samuel Aubrey dies and is buried in Hereford Cathedral.
New Model Army defeats Royalists at Naseby; King Charles visits Hereford; the Scots Army besiege Hereford for six weeks; Clehonger Manor taken; King returns to Hereford.
December 1645 Colonel John Birch takes Hereford and the city plundered; eight hundred people taken prisoner.

1646

Birch declares martial law; Goodrich Castle, the last of the Royalist strongholds, under the command of Colonel Henry Lingen falls.
Oxford surrenders to Roundheads; the King tries to escape, but fails.

1647

Herbert's father is fined £500 by the Roundheads.

1648

Parliament votes to bring Charles I to trial

1651

Herbert the Queen's College Oxford 10 November 1651; (Sir) Joseph Williamson a fellow student.

1653

Herbert and his cousin Herbert Westfaling both admitted to Grays Inn on 14 November 1653.

1656

Herbert's brother Godwin in Smyrna Turkey with Captain George Swanley, a mariner and Essex landowner. Witnesses his will.

1657

Herbert's older sister Anne marries William Boothby at St Pancras in Soper Lane; Herbert's sister Mary dies; Godwin in Smirna at the death of Captain Swanley.

1659

George Booth's rebellion. Lewis Audley disperses the abortive Royalist rising in Surrey.

1660

Parliament invites Charles II to return to England. Herbert Westfaling a Member of the Convention Parliament.

1661

Disputed election to the Cavalier Parliament involving Sir Henry Lingen and Herbert Westfaling; Militia Acts introduced; Herbert's father nominated as Sheriff.

1662

Herbert marries Joyce Brydges, the daughter of John Brydges of Priors Court;

Herbert's kinsman Roger Vaughan returned as M.P. for Hereford.

1663

Herbert enlarges his landholding.

1664

Herbert Aubrey III born. Herbert's father makes his will; Herbert writing regularly to (Sir) Joseph Williamson; Herbert's father taxed on thirteen hearths.

1665

The great plague of London; Herbert's brother Godwin certifies Captain Swanley's will, made in Smyrna.

1666

The great fire of London. Herbert's daughter Joyce born.

1668

Joyce's father John Brydges dies 7 August 1668.

1669

Herbert's son Brydges born. His Great-Aunt Mary Rudhall dies.

1670

Rudhall inheritance challenged. Herbert sells Priors Court to Paul Foley. Herbert and Humphrey Cornewall stand surety for Roger Vaughan as Collector of the Hearth Tax.

1671

Herbert made Receiver of Taxes. Herbert's father dies 22 December 1671.

1672

Roger Vaughan dies 28 May 1672. Herbert and Humphrey Cornewall find themselves in debt to the Crown for £1,800; Stop of the Exchequer; cash payments suspended for twelve months.

1673

Herbert in grave financial difficulties; Lord Danby Lord High Treasurer.

Salt & Silk

1674

Herbert's mother makes her will.

1675

Herbert receives letters threatening him with Exchequer process.

1676

Influenza epidemic in England. Herbert's mother dies; Herbert stands surety for John Davis. Herbert's son Reginald born.

1677

Treasury finds Herbert's accounts to be £1,548 in arrears and he is replaced by William Bowdler.

1678

The 'Popish Plot' leads to anti-Catholic hysteria; Lord Danby implicated.

1679

Herbert secretly writes to Lord Danby in the Tower; Herbert's Uncle Anthony dies.

1680

Herbert Chairman of Quarter Sessions. Death of Robert Pye of the Mynde.

1681

Herbert returned as M.P. for Hereford with the Exclusionist Paul Foley; Parliament meets in Oxford to avoid the rioting in London.

1682

Herbert made an Alderman; his son Herbert III enters the Queen's College Oxford 18 December 1682.

1683

Herbert a Deputy Lord Lieutenant of the County of Hereford; the great freeze allows the Thames to be used as a vast fairground.

1684

Herbert made Captain of Militia Horse and Freeman of Monmouth; Secretary of State Jenkins resigns the Seals.

1685

James II succeeds his brother Charles II; the Duke of Monmouth's rebellion; Monmouth defeated and beheaded; Judge George Jeffreys (1648-1689) conducts 'Bloody Assizes' against Monmouth's followers.
Herbert returned unopposed as M.P. for Hereford; Herbert's brother Godwin marries Jane Clark at Brampton Abbots 11 Dec 1685.

1686

Lemuel Kingdon dies and is buried St Giles in the Fields 19 February 1686; Herbert appointed to Kingdon's vacancy on the Irish Revenue Commission at the instigation of Lord Rochester.

1687

Lord Rochester dismissed. Earl of Clarendon recalled from Ireland and Lord Tyrconnel takes his place.

Herbert returns briefly to England to clear his account of the Hearth Tax.

1688

Seven English lords invite William of Orange to England (Lord Danby among them). James II escapes to France.

1689

Herbert returns to England; the Earl of Shrewsbury orders his arrest on his arrival at Chester.

1690

King William III defeats his father-in-law at the Battle of the Boyne.

1691

Herbert's son Reginald enters Balliol College Oxford 31 March 1691; Herbert's brother Godwin makes his will and dies this year.

Herbert dies and is buried at Clehonger 9 November 1691.

APPENDIX C
Some of Morgan Aubrey's
Relations, Friends & Associates

Joan daughter of Robert Vaux of Cumberland	Morgan's wife
Francis Vaux, Merchant Taylor	Joan's brother
Robert Vaux, Merchant Taylor	Joan's brother
Samuel Aubrey	Morgan's only surviving son & heir
Joyce daughter of William Rudhall of Rudhall	Samuel's wife
Herbert Aubrey	their son & heir, the 'Old Cavelier'
Morgan Aubrey	their son, slain in Irland
Anthony Aubrey	their son, fought as a Royalist
Joane Aubrey	their daughter
Katherine Aubrey (Kate)	Morgan's only surviving daughter
Dr Francis Bevans D.C.L, M.P. (Frank)	her first husband
Aubrey Bevans	their son
Sir William Herbert	her second husband
Sir Anthony St John	her third husband
Oliver St John	their son
John Aubrey, Clothworker of London	Morgan's uncle
Joan Aubrey	his wife
Joan Taylor	Morgan's sister
William Taylor, of London	her husband
Martha Taylor	their daughter
Elizabeth Taylor	their daughter
Hopkyn Aubrey of Llangiwg	Morgan's brother
Dr William Aubrey, Maser of Requests, etc	Morgan's cousin
Wilgliford Aubrey	his wife
Hugh George	William's 'loving and trustie servant'
John Cooke	Morgan's kitchen boy
Joan Sheffell	Morgan's servant
George Samwell	Morgan's 'loving friend'
Dr John Dee, astronomer, alchemist, etc	Morgan's friend
Sir Michael Blunt, Knight Lt. of the Tower of London	Morgan's associate

Some of Herbert Aubrey II's
Relations, Friends & Associates

Joyce daughter of John Brydges of Priors Court	Herbert's wife
Herbert Aubrey III	their son & heir
Brydges Aubrey	their son
Reginald Aubrey	their son
Joyce Aubrey	their daughter
Elizabeth Aubrey	their daughter
(Sir) Samuel Aubrey	Herbert's grandfather
Joyce Aubrey née Rudhall	Herbert's grandmother
Herbert Aubrey	Herbert's father, the 'Old Cavalier'
Elizabeth Aubrey (née Bedell)	his mother
Anthony Aubrey	his uncle
Morgan Aubrey	his uncle
Joane Emley née Aubrey	his aunt
Anne Boothby née Aubrey	his sister
Samuel Aubrey	his older brother
Mary Aubrey	his sister
Elizabeth Aubrey	his sister
Matthew Aubrey	his brother
Godwin Aubrey	his brother
Thomas Aubrey	his brother
Margaret Carpenter née Brydges	Joyce Aubrey's sister
Theodosia Kingdon née Carpenter	her daughter
Lemuel Kingdon, M.P.	Theodosia's husband
Dorothy Thomas née Brydges	Joyce Aubrey's sister
Ralph Hawtrey Jnr	Herbert's cousin
Herbert Westfaling M.P.	Herbert's cousin and close friend
Robert Pye of the Mynde	his kinsman
Roger Vaughan, M.P.	his kinsman

Sources & Notes

Bibliography

Adair, John *Roundhead General, The Campaigns of Sir William Waller* (1997)
Barber, Richard ed. *John Aubrey Brief Lives* (1982)
Barty-King, Hugh *The Salters' Company 1394-1994* (1994)
Beavan, Rev Alfred B. *The Aldermen of the City of London* (1913)
Benbos, R. Mark, ed. *Index of London Citizens involved in City Government 1558-1603 (1965)*
Bisschop, W.R. *The Rise of the London Money Market 1640-1826* (1968)
Boyd's *Citizens of London*
Braudel, Fernand *The Structures of Everyday Life* Vol I (1981)
Camden Society *Anecdotes & Traditions* (1839)
Carlton, Charles *The Court of Orphans* (1974)
Colburn, Henry ed. *Ellis Correspondence 1686-1688* (1828)
Dale, T.C. *The Inhabitants of London 1638* (1931)
Dudley, Jasper *The Tudor Age* (1988)
Duncombe, *History and Antiquities of Hereford* (1812)
Faraday, M.A. ed. *Hereford Militia Assessments of 1663* (1972)
Fitzpatrick, Thomas *The Bloody Bridge* (1903)
Forrest, H.E. *Rudhal,* (1916)
Gardiner. J & Wenborn, N. eds.*The History Today Companion to British History* (1995)
Gwynor Jones, J., *Early Modern Wales* (1994)
Henning, B.D. ed. *The House of Commons 1660-1690* (1983)
Hibbert, Christopher *The English, Social History 1066-1945* (1988)
Hibbert, Christopher *Cavaliers & Roundheads* (1994)
Hickson, Mary *The Irish Massacres of 1641* Vol 1 (1884)
Hill, Christopher *The Century of Revolution 1603-1714* (1980)
Hopkins, Lisa *Elizabeth I and her Court* (1990)
Houlbrooke, Ralph A. *The English Family 1450-1700* (1984)
Johnson, Richard *Ancient Customs of Hereford* (1882)
Latham, Robert ed. *The Illustrated Pepys* (2000)
Laurence, Anne *Women in England 1500-1750, A Social History* (1996)
Lindley, Keith *Popular Politics & Religion in Civil War London* (1997)
Lewis, E.A. *Early Chancery Proceedings* (1937)
Melton, Frank T. *Sir Robert Clayton and the Origins of English Deposit Banking, 1658-1685* (1986)

Morgan, Kenneth O. ed. *The Oxford History of Britain* (1993)
Morrice, J.C. *Early Modern Wales* (1908)
Neale, J.E. *Queen Elizabeth I* (1961)
Newman, P.R. *Royalist Officers in England and Wales 1642-1660* (1981)
Parker, Derek *John Donne & his world* (1975)
Peacock, John *The Chronicle of Western Costume* (1996)
Plowden, Alison *Women all on Fire* (1998)
Porter, Roy *London, A Social History* (1994)
Robinson, Rev. Charles J. *A History of the Castles of Herefordshire and Their Lords* (1863)
Robinson, Rev. Charles J. *A History of the Mansions and Manors of Herefordshire* (1872)
Rowse, A.L. *The Tower of London in the History of the Nation* (1974)
Shoesmith, Ron *The Civil War in Hereford* (1995)
Simms, J.G. *Jacobite Ireland 1685-91* (1969)
Thomas, Keith *Religion and the Decline of Magic* (1971)
University of Wales *Early Chancery Proceedings* (1937)
Vansittart, Peter *In Memory of England* (1998)
Wilding, Michael *Raising Spirits Making Gold and Swapping Wives* (1999)
Woodhead, J.R. *The Rulers of London 1660-1689* (1965)

Alumni Oxiensis
Dictionary of National Biography
Flagellum Parliamentarium: Sarcastic Notes on 200 M.P.s 1661-1678
Victoria County History of Bedfordshire, Buckinghamshire, Herefordshire, and Surrey

National Archives (PRO)

Calendar of Patent Rolls 1571/2 C66/1089/2882
Calendar of State Papers Domestic Series 1661-1662, 1664-1665, 1666-1667, 1675-1676, 1676-1677, 1677-1678, 1680-1681, 1682, 1683.
Calendar of Treasury Books 1675, 1680, 1680-1681.
C10/146/3
C115/100, No. 7489 Some time before 1623, George Scudamore wrote to Sir John Scudamore, his brother, deploring the 'flightiness' of the latter's daughter Elizabeth, and recommended 'Madam Pye or my ladie Aubrie (gentlewomen of great sobrietie)' to ' tame' the young gentlewoman, who, according to Scudamore, had more need of a good marriage than a 'new fashioned gowne'.
Deed GG 574, 18 Jan, 43 Eliz: (1600-1) concerning Hugh George of New Brayneford, Middlesex, gent. and the estate of Dr William Aubrey.

E179/251/16 – Subsidy Roll - St Mary Abchurch Subsidy Rolls show that Morgan Aubrey was only one of six prosperous people listed. In the Subsidy Rolls of 1568 for London, Morgan Aubrey's name is only one of six listed in the parish as being assessed at £60. The subsidy rolls in 1582 show he had £50 or more in goods and £10 per annum or more in lands etc. and his property was valued at £50, making it one of the most valuable in the parish. From being taxed 50 shillings in 1582, he paid 60 shillings in 1589.

Corporation of London Record Office
Court of Aldermen Repertories 1560, R14,431,b

Guildhall Library, Corporation of London
GL Ms 7666
St Mary Abchurch baptism, marriage and burial records

Family Record Centre – P.C.C. Wills
Hopkin Aubrey 1580 PROB 11/62
Dr William Aubrey 1595 PROB 11/86
Francis Bevans 1602 PROB 11/100
Robert Vaux 16 Apr 1608 PROB 11/112/57
Morgan Aubrey Salter of London 1608 PROB 11/112
Joan Aubrey 1613 PROB 11/121
Mathew Bedell 1636 PROB 11/172
Mary Aubrey's Administration 1657 PROB 6/33/156
John Brydges of Priors Court 1669 PROB 11/331

International Genealogical Index (IGI)

Clehonger
A village in Herefordshire about four miles south west from the city of Hereford, close to the banks of the River Wye.
According to the Hearth Tax records, in 1664, 41 houses stood there, 19 of which were charged with the tax. The largest house, Clehonger Manor, where the Aubreys lived until the late eighteenth century when it was completely destroyed by fire, had 13 hearths. One house in the village had 7 hearths, one 4, one 2, and 14 houses had only 1 hearth.

The Salters' Company Charter of King James I gave

> '*the power of survey, search, correction and governance over all persons exercising the Art or Mistery of the Salters and of all wares etc exposed for sale within the City of London, its suburbs and within two miles of the City. And if such wares and merchandizes ... shall be found to be unwholesome corrupt or unworthy to be sold or if any such weights and measures belonging or pertaining to any such person or persons using and exercising the Art .. on any such search shall be found to be false deceitful and unlawful that then it shall be lawful ... to seize such wares and merchandizes and to dispose of them according to the Laws of England and the custom of the City of London.*
>
> *And it shall be lawful ... to break and spoil all such false deceitful and unlawful weights and measures on any such search ... and to punish the offender or offenders and to correct the default and defaults in that behalf found according to the Laws and Customs of our Kingdom of England.*'

(*The Charter of King James I and the Ordinances of the Worshipful Company of Salters*, London 1896)

Joan Aubrey's will:

Since c1612, the Company of Salters have had the use of Joan Aubrey's £100, plus the residue of the interest of 10 shillings after the annual distribution of £4-10s-0d to the 'poore widdowes', 'for ever', i.e. up to now, over 390 years.

Leaving aside the original £100, calculating the compound interest for that length of time even on 10 shillings, leads to more digits than one can easily accommodate on a calculator.

American economist Bryan Taylor has estimated that £1 invested in British Government gilts in 1700 would have grown to £629,933 by 1995, but the same sum invested on the British stock market would have yielded £51,554,158.

Joan's £100 plus 0.5% per cent or 10 shillings accruing per annum, for another eighty eight years, to bring the calculation up to 1700, gives the amount of £144 which sum, if then invested by the Company on the stock market, would have produced a staggering amount of money today. Given such bequests, one can understand and admire the size and splendour of the huge building of the Company of Salters that now proudly rises above its neighbours in Fore Street in the City of London!

Salt & Silk

Index

Audley, Lewis, Parliamentarian, 93, 106, 109-10
Audley, Mary née Boothby, 93, 106

Ball, Henry, 123
Balliol College, Oxford, 186, 208, 217
Bankes, Lady Mary, née Hawtrey, 106
Barbados, 158-159, 162
Barlow, Thomas, Chaplain, 29
Beaufort, Duke of, 196-197
Bedawe, Owen ap Jevan, 50
Bedell, Anne née Boothby, 64
Bedell, Elizabeth née Bird, 68
Bedell, Mary, 104, 104
Bedell, Mathew, Merchant Taylor, 64, 68, 105, 106, 109
Bedell, Prudence, 105
Behn, Aphra, 149, n155, 189, 201
Bertie, the Hon. Charles, 149, 151, 192, 195, 203-204, 207
Bertie, Mary née Tryon, 149, 192, 195
Bertie, the Hon. Peregrine, 195
Bevan, Richard, 73, 95
Bevans, Aubrey, 31, 43, 50, 56-57
Bevans, Francis (Frank), 29-30, 33, 41, 42-43, 56
Birch, Colonel John, 89-90, 91, 96-97, 128, 141-143, 150, 159, 167, 170, 171, 173, 182,
      183, 184, 207
Black Friars, 129
Blunt, Sir Michael, 34
Bodenham, John, 160-162
Bonner, Edward, Bishop of London, 11
Boothall Inn, 184-185
Boothby, Anne née Aubrey, 57, 58, 59, 64, 65, 66, 68, 71, 73, 75, 76, 78, 80, 81, 83, 86,
      87, 88, 98, 99, 102, 103, 106, 132, 145
Boothby, William, Merchant Taylor, 103, 106
Bosworth, Dr Roger, 111
Bowdler, William, 140, 151, 167, 168
Bowling Green Close, 121
Boyne, 213, 216
Brampton Abbotts, 42, 116, 145, 150, 198
Bridgecourt Farm, 41, 42-43
Bristol, 78, 213
Broughton, Katherine née Rudhall, 62, 133
Broughton, Richard of Owlebury, 62
Bruce, Lord, 201
Brydges, John of Priors Court, 118, 132, 135, 136, 137, 172
Brydges, Joyce née Bright, 135, 137
Brydges, Thomas of Old Colwall, 166
Brydges, Marshall, 137
Brydges, William, 159, 182, 189, 206
Brydges, William of Tibberton Court, 118

Carpenter, Thomas of Lincoln's Inn, 119, 135, 136, 137, 138, 164
Carpenter, Margaret née Brydges, 119, 135, 164, 190

Salt & Silk

Gresham, Sir Thomas, 25, 26-27, n27
Grey, Henry, Duke of Suffolk, 10
Grey, Lady Katherine, 28-29
Greyfriars, 65, 75, 81, 82, 95, 120, 142
Greys Inn, 101, 156
Grindal, Edmund, Archbishop of Canterbury, 20, 21
Gwynn, Nell, 189

Hampton Court, 173, 179, 180, 182
Harcourt, Sir Robert, 38
Harford, Bridstock, 118, 166, 167
Harford, Bridstock Dr. 118, 119, 166-167
Harford, Elizabeth née Brydges, 118, 166
Harley, Sir Edward, 113, 159, 169, 176, 184
Harvey, Sir Stephen, 193
Hatton, Sir John, 108
Hatton, Sir Robert, 108
Hawtrey, Mary, (see Bedell)
Hawtrey, Ralph, 104, 108, 109
Hawtrey, Ralph, Merchant Taylor, 104, 105, 106, 109
Hearne, Gilbert of Hereford, 199, 217
Hearne, Joyce née Aubrey (see Aubrey, Joyce)
Henley, Hugh, 17
Henrietta Maria, Queen, 70
Henry VII, King, 101
Henry VIII, King, 6
Herbert, Henry, Earl of Pembroke, 19, 21, 28, 90
Herbert, Sir Richard of Cwmystwith, 5
Herbert, Sir William, 43-44, 57
Hereford, 75, 76, 77, 79, 81, 82, 86, 87, 88, 89, 91, 96, 97, 101, 102, 111, 114, 118, 130,
    135, 137, 142, 165, 167, 168, 170, 177, 182, 193, 196, 205, 211
Hereford Assizes, 95, 182, 205
Hereford Castle, 95
Hereford Cathedral, 82, 90, 116, 121,
Hereford Hospital, 119
Hereford Quarter Sessions, 156
Hereford School, 85, 97
Herefordshire, 142, 152, 178, 182
Holman, Nicholas, 14
Holman, Simon of Stratton, 14
Holme Lacy, 79, 178, 179
Holmes, Sir Robert, 174, n175, 189, 190, 200, 201, 202, 205, 206, 207
Hopton, Sir Edward, 112-115, 124
Hoskyns, Sir John, 182, 199
Howard, Anne, 127
Howard, Thomas Lord Arundel, 127
Hull, Susan, servant, 136, 137
Hyde, Anne, 143, 166, 172, 210
Hyde Park, London, 142

Irish Revenue Commission, 190, 206, 207, 213

Quakers, 183
Queen's College, Oxford, 97, 101, 123, 157, 170, 171-172, 186

Raleigh, Sir Walter, 38, 39
Ranelagh, Lord, 165, 190, 201, 202, 203
Raven, Miles, 17
Richard II, King, 12
Rich, Henry, Earl of Holland, 108
Richmond, Duke of 148
Rochester, Lord, 53, 143, 166, 184, 206, 208, 210
Rogers, John, 11
Ross, 99
Royal Africa Company, 159
Rudhall, Bartholomew, 134-135
Rudhall, Gilbert, 60
Rudhall, John, M.P., 60, 61, 132,
Rudhall Manor, 59, 63, 99, 116, 132, 133, 134
Rudhall, Margaret née Croft, 101
Rudhall, Mary, 63, 69, 98, 99, 110, 112, 114, 116, 122, 126, 132, 133, 134, 135
Rudhall, Sir Richard, 39, 41, 60
Rudhall, William, Attorney-General, 59
Rudhall, William of Rudhall, 41, 42, 60, 69, 101
Rudhall, William, Colonel, 60, 61, 96, 98, 99-100
Rupert, Prince, 79, 98
Rushout, Sir James, 215
Rye, 199

St Giles in the Fields, 206
St Mary Abchurch, 14, 16, 17, 23, 30, 37, 40, 44, 47, 48
St Mary the Virgin, 98
St John, Sir Anthony, 57
St John, Oliver, 57
St John, Oliver, Parliamentarian, 93
St Pancras Church, Soper Lane, 103
St Peter, Dormington, 119

Salters Fraternity, 12, 14, 20, 32, 38, 39, 40, 48-49
Samwell, George, 49
Savage, Richard Lord Rivers, 195
Scudamore, Sir Barnabas, 80, 81, 82, 83, 86, 88, 90, 97,
Scudamore, James, 40, 78
Scudamore, John, 41, 42
Scudamore, Sir John, 113
Scudamore, Lady, 78, 178-181
Scudamore, Lord, 77, 78, 79, 96, 169, 176, 177, 178, 179-181, 184
Seymour, Edward, Earl of Hertford, 6, 7, 28
Seymour, Sir Edward, 190, 207
Seymour, Henry, 129
Shaftsbury, Lord, 144, n147, 169, 176, 191, 194-195
Sheffell, Joan, 15, 16
Shelwyck, 47, 66, 97

Shrewsbury, Earl of, 53, 212
Sign of the Black Swan, 14, 15, 28, 30, 35, 48, 49, 66
Snodhill Park, 141, 145
Spencer, Edward, 42
Stamford, Earl of, 75, 76
Stoke Edith, 137, 138
Stoke Say Castle, 101
Strafford, Earl of, 70, n74, 154, n155
Suron, Jaques, 99
Suron, Marie, 99-100
Swanley, George, Captain, 103, 129, 199

Talbot, Sir John, 196
Taylor, Elizabeth, 43
Taylor, Joan née Aubrey, 8
Taylor, William, 8
The Friars, 64, 94
Thomas, Dorothy née Brydges, 119, 135, 136, 137, 138
Thomas, Walter of Swansea, 119, 135
Thorold, Thomas, 105
Tompkyns, Anne, 128
Tompkyns, Mary née Pye, 128
Tompkyns, Thomas of Monnington-on-Wye, 128
Tower of London, 154, 194
Trant, Patrick, 182
Trinity College, 213
Trumbull, George, 210
Trumbull, Sir William, 210
Tryon, James, 195
Tryon, Mary née Stydolph, 195
Tryon, Peter of Harringworth, 192
Tyrconnel, Earl of, 208-209, 210, 212, 213

Vaughan, Frances née Pye, 126
Vaughan, Henry of Bredwardine & Moccas, 126
Vaughan, John, 40
Vaughan, Margaret, 130
Vaughan, Roger, 115, 126-128, 129-132, 139, 141, 146, 170, 171
Vaux, John, Merchant Taylor, 13, 14, 16
Vaux, Robert, 49
Vickers, Thomas, 49
Villiers, Francis, 108

Waller, Sir William, 76-77, n78, 79, 80, 101, 193
Walsingham, Sir Francis, 20, 36, 55
Walter, Lucy, 166
Weobley, 170
Westfaling, Anne née Barlow, 29
Westfaling, Anne, née Edwards, 117, 122, 133, 134
Westfaling, Frances née Rudhall, 56, 61, 112, 116
Westfaling, Herbert, Bishop, 29, 31